'Lily Wong' Is Sent Packing After Barb Tossed at Beijing

By Don Hagerty
Staff Reporter

HONG KONG — In a cartoon published here last Thursday, Larry Feign joked that cartoonists might be executed once China regains sovereignty over Hong Kong in 1997.

As it turns out, Mr. Feign didn't have to wait that long. His newspaper cartoon strip, "The World of Lily Wong," got the chop Friday, stirring fears about self-censorship in the local press. The South China Morning Post, which had published the strip for eight years, sent a fax to Mr. Feign Friday evening announcing that it was being canceled, effective immediately.

The Post offered no explanation to readers in its edition Monday. But David Armstrong, editor of the newspaper, said in a telephone interview that "Lily Wong" was dropped as part of a cost-cutting drive. He dismissed suggestions that the Post wanted to eliminate a cartoon whose barbs at China's alleged sales of...

black humor about China's alleged sales of kidneys, eyes and other organs from executed prisoners. In one of the episodes, a cartoon character is sentenced to death after agreeing with a prison guard that Chinese Premier Li Peng is "a fascist murderous dog."

Aside from bashing China's political leaders, Mr. Feign's cartoons often pilloried British of...

Hong Kong Lily killed off

Hong Kong's English-language media became duller yesterday when the South China Morning Post axed The World of Lily Wong, an irreverent cartoon strip that cast a sardonic eye over Hong Kong in advance of its transfer to Chinese rule in 1997. The decision, portrayed as a cost-cutting measure, raised concerns about media self-censorship, as Lily Wong was often critical of the Chinese Communist party. The cartoon appeared for the last time on Saturday, when it featured alleged trade in organs for transplants from executed prisoners. Mr Larry Feign, draughtsman and author of the cartoon, said: "I personally do not get the feeling the budget is the reason."

Last year, Mr Rupert Murdoch, chief executive of News Corporation, dropped the BBC World Service from satellite television broadcasts into China and north Asia on his Star TV network. Subsequently, he admitted the decision was taken for political reasons.

The local newspaper industry is, however, about to get a shot in the arm when Mr Jimmy Lai, one of Hong Kong's more colourful entrepreneurs, launches Apple Daily next month. Mr Lai has vowed to make the most of the next two years of comparative freedom under British rule.

Simon Holberton, Hong Kong

Mystery death of Lily Wong

ROM STEPHEN VINES
Hong Kong

...hout a word of explanation by Wong, and her American husband, Stuart, have become non-persons. But Hong Kong's...

Jokes such as this against the Chinese are believed to have prompted the ending of the strip in Hong

Hong Kong: The Demise of Lily Wong

THE WORLD OF LILY Wong" chronicled Hong Kong six days a week, four frames a day. For eight years the cartoon strip's creator, American Larry Feign, lampooned Beijing bureaucrats and British colonial officials alike in the pages of the South China Morning Post. Then, on May 19, Feign and his strip were unceremoniously axed.

The Post, now owned by Robert Kuok, a Malaysian-Chinese tycoon with close ties to Beijing, says the decision to fire Feign was part of a cost-cutting drive which included plans to lay off 25 editorial staff members. One wonders. The cartoonist was sacked a few days before everybody else. Could his last series, focusing on China's alleged trade in the organs of executed prisoners, have had something to do with it?

Those in Hong Kong who worry about the press's creeping self-censorship in the run-up to China's resumption of

sovereignty in 1997 have long pointed to "Lily Wong" as a bellwether of China's tolerance for criticism. All seemed well as recently as November, when Feign's contract was renewed. It may never be clear exactly who or what prompted the change of heart. What does seem clear is that, in the words of Feign, after 1997 "Hong Kong will become an uncomfortable place for people like me." The loss of his wit will diminish the comfort level for everyone else.

anti-Beijing cartoonist loses job

JONATHAN MIRSKY

...UTE about self-censorship by the Hong ...ss in deference to ...as broken out... ...essal of the col... ...wn political car... ...the leading Eng... ...newspaper. ...Feign, the creator ...p, a notoriously ir... ...strip, which has b... ...the South Chi... ...Post for more th... ...rs, has been fire... ...said Armstrong ...made to budgetary ...Kong Governor Chr... ...cartoon strip, on ...Feign saying "I foll... ...of 'Lily' daily."

...eiling members of the ...cil have expressed a ...issal. In a letter to... ...he said that after t... ...to China, "even in Ho... ...one country with two... ...sense of humour." ...said yesterday: "This... ...raght from my heart, I... ...has died. I can't beli... ...it's most profitable par... ...or budgetary reasons. I... ...to take a pay cut but the... ...it doesn't add up." ...the cartoon strip was...

DER SPIEGEL
Nr.22/29.5.95 · 5,00
PANORAMA

Anti-Peking-Cartoon eingestellt

Hongkong

Die Übernahme der Kronkolonie Hongkong durch China am 1. Juli 1997 hat ein erstes Opfer gefordert: Lily ...hat ein Comic strip der englisch...

Pekings kommunistische F... KP-Patriarch Deng Xiaop... Woche eingestellt. Sie sei... posten" in der reaktion... rechnung gewesen, ließ d... tion der South China ... verlauten, die im abgel... jahr 120 Millionen ... machte. Hongkongs... band, der einen "gen... Selbstzensur" befürc... hand. Die demnächst a... Portugiesisch-China...

...lay auf Seite 10

KÖNNEN SIE ALLEN ORGANBESTELLUNGEN NACHKOMMEN?

KEIN PROBLEM, WIR HABEN ZWEI JAHRE NACHSCHUB IN DEN TODESZELLEN.

UND WAS, WENN DER AUSPEBRAUCHT IST?

Disappearance of 'famous increases jitters in Hong K

POLITICS   NEWSWEEK JUNE 5, 1995

JONATHAN MANTHORPE
Vancouver Sun Correspondent

Satirical cartoon's demise linked to imminent takeover by Beijing

HONG KONG
...n the jittery atmosphere here

Wong decision strips Hong Kong of humour

Catherine Field in Hong Kong

ILY WONG, the most bitingly satirical voice on China in Hong Kong, has been stilled. The cartoon strip, which poked fun at Deng Xiaoping, the barons fighting for power in Beijing, and the People's Liberation Army, has been dropped from the pages of Hong Kong's leading English-language newspaper, the South China Morning Post.

The demise of the popular World of Lily Wong ...

satirised Hong Kong's bureaucrats and British expatriates.

"I personally don't get the feeling budget is the real reason," Lily Wong's creator, Larry Feign, said.

The Post's editor in chief, David Armstrong, denied the cartoon had been scrapped for political reasons. "Lily Wong is a particularly big ticket item. Larry Feign is quite well paid," he said. "Lily Wong became a casualty of the economy drive.

The Post's one ...

Feign immediately offered to work for a much lower fee but was rejected. "I had already completed and submitted my cartoons to appear this week. The editor declined to run them even though they are paid for," he said.

Lily Wong's demise comes at a sensitive time for Hong Kong's media. With the hand-over to China two years away, human rights monitors have ...

Comic Stripped From Hong Kong Pape

...and close links to Beijing, bough ...paper in 1993 from media ...Rupert Murdoch, who admitted ...to placate Beijing and protect his ...lite TV interests in China.

Journalists at the Post said that ...had not interfered with covera... ...he bought the paper and that ...thing, editorials became more ...under his control. Editor ...insists that he alone decided ...cut, although Kuok recently... ...that the Hong Kong press sho... ...confrontation with Beijing.

Fans of the 'Doonesbury of Asia' fear that the pointed cartoon's demise may have been politically motivated.

By MAGGIE FARLEY
SPECIAL TO THE TIMES

HONG KONG—Larry Feign's car toon, "The World of Lily Wong, has often brought a smile or two over breakfast with its satire of daily life and the politics in Hong Kong. But the cartoon has disappeared from the territory's

One call ...
family and ...

政治漫畫家

本報封殺

八十年代香港的「南

華早報」，美國漫畫家

Feign的一系列描繪中

國政治和社會現象（Larry

的漫畫...

Most of the cartoons in this book appeared previously in the *South China Morning Post*. And those that didn't, should have.

This is a book of cartoons and satire. No attempt is made to usurp, damage or slander the name and/or image of any fictional character, trademark, or living person.

ISBN 962 7866 09 1

Published 1995 by

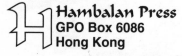 **Hambalan Press**
GPO Box 6086
Hong Kong

printed in the British Crown Colony of Hong Kong

This book was produced entirely with a **Digital DECpc XL566 computer** and a **Hewlett-Packard ScanJet IIc scanner**. Who says you need a Macintosh for graphics?

BANNED IN HONG KONG

written and illustrated by
Larry Feign

edited by
Cathy Sau Yung Tsang-Feign,
MA MFCC

to Lily ♥

CONTENTS

ONE COUNTRY, TWO SYSTEMS
— BUT NO SENSE OF HUMOUR
by
MARTIN C.M. LEE, Q.C.

The following is an expansion of a letter from Mr. Martin Lee to the South China Morning Post which the newspaper has, to date, declined to print.

In Hong Kong our rights and freedoms will not be lost all at once. They will be sacrificed one by one.

In his eight years drawing the cartoon strip "The World of Lily Wong" for the *South China Morning Post*, Larry Feign has depicted — with sometimes devastating accuracy — the foibles of the Hong Kong and Chinese Governments, Hong Kong's political classes and ordinary Hong Kong people. In the long tradition of political cartooning, he has lampooned everyone from Deng Xiaoping to various Hong Kong governors to me.

Although we may never have the full background for why Lily Wong was given her walking papers at the end of May 1995, no one at the *South China Morning Post* has suggested it was because the comic strip was no longer amusing. In fact, it has been suggested that the final series on the sale of organs in China was just a little bit *too* funny and close to the truth for comfort for the Chinese authorities.

The Hong Kong Journalists Association has annually reported the escalating trend toward self-censorship in our local media. In the wake of the arrest and imprisonment of Hong Kong journalist Xi Yang and well-documented cases of self-censorship at both of Hong Kong's television stations, TVB and ATV, and other local news providers, press freedom has never been more under siege. The international media has been no exception: after STAR TV owner (and former *South China Morning Post* owner) Rupert Murdoch observed that totalitarian regimes cannot long withstand the liberating forces of information, China began enforcing a law prohibiting satellite dishes. Mr. Murdoch dumped the offending BBC World Service faster than you can say "kowtow," acknowledging as he did so that his actions were principally to access the giant China market. At least he was honest about it.

Sadly, the phenomenon I term "bending before the north wind has begun to blow" is by no means limited to the media. We see it in daily life, in business, and of course, in politics. Politicians in particular have — or should have — dicey relations with political cartoonists. In my time in politics, I have certainly been the subject of some very unflattering cartoons. But if we in Hong Kong and Asia really believe in free speech and a free society, that must mean we will be prepared to defend equally the right of cartoonists and commentators to make fun of democrats, Communist Party officials or the Governor.

The reality is that the Joint Declaration's guarantees for freedom of speech and the press are in practice worthless unless newspaper proprietors, editors and journalists are prepared to stand up for press freedom. Cartoonists are journalists too, and although humour is not a freedom expressly guaranteed by the Joint Declaration and the Basic Law, political cartoons are clearly a form of expression and as such should be protected as any other form of speech. But the jettison-ing of Mr. Feign's daily comic strip raises the question of whether we in Hong Kong will have "one country, two systems" — but no sense of humour.

Hong Kong does not need "free speech with Chinese characteristics." China and its emis-saries like Mr. Lu Ping have been working overtime to reassure Hong Kong and the world that Hong Kong will be allowed to continue as a thriving commercial and financial centre. But Hong Kong's competitiveness is directly linked with our ability to receive and process new information — whether by computer, newspaper, television, radio or political cartoons. It is the free market in information and ideas that underpins our free market system itself.

Most important, Hong Kong's media serves the vital public function of keeping the public informed and keeping politicians and the business community more or less honest. I hope that Hong Kong's free-wheeling and sometimes intemperate press will stay that way. I may not always like what they have to say, but the alternative is much worse to contemplate.

I hope also that Beijing will see the good sense of a good sense of humour. But ultimately, the lessons from Lily Wong are not just for journalists, but for all of us who will soon be under Chinese sovereignty. There are no ironclad guarantees of our rights and freedoms. They will last only as long as we as a community are prepared to commit ourselves to making certain that our free-doms: of the press, of expression — of humour — survive.

One observer, Martin Niemoeller, described the gradual loss of freedom in Nazi Germany thus:

"In Germany, they came first for the Communists and I didn't speak up because I wasn't a Communist. Then they came for the Jews, and I didn't speak up because I wasn't a Jew. Then they came for the trade unions, and I didn't speak up because I wasn't a trade unionist. Then they came for the Catholics, and I didn't speak up because I was a Protestant. Then they came for me, and by that time no one was left to speak up."

Hong Kong's free press, open debate and free flow of information are some of the greatest treasures China will be bequeathed in 1997. Let us hope there is still something left to inherit.

Martin Lee, Q.C., one of Hong Kong's leading barristers, is Chairman of the Democratic Party of Hong Kong and a directly elected member of the Legislative Council.

THE CARTOONS YOU WEREN'T SUPPOSED TO SEE

by Larry Feign

"The World of Lily Wong" first appeared in the *Hongkong Standard* in November 1986. In December 1987 the strip moved to the *South China Morning Post*, where, except for a nine-month hiatus in 1991, it appeared daily until it was abruptly terminated, appearing for the last time on May 20, 1995.

In its eight-year existence, Lily Wong and I enjoyed considerable editorial freedom. Nevertheless, there were times when cartoons were returned to me by editors as unacceptable, and even several occasions when cartoons were removed from the paper at the last minute, leaving a blank space where a comic strip should have been.

One of my earliest attempts at injecting politics into "The World of Lily Wong" was rejected by the *Hongkong Standard*. The cartoon below, referring to a well-known hostess club in Kowloon, was supposed to appear on October 22, 1987. The editor, Robert Chow, declined to run it, but not because of its political message. He thought the implied language was obscene and inappropriate for a "family" newspaper.

For the first year, Lily Wong was not a political cartoon strip. The lives of Lily, her family and her then-suitor Stuart revolved around East-West culture clash and everyday annoyances in Hong Kong. When Lily moved to the *South China Morning Post*, the comic strip took on a more political tone. The editor, John Dux, made it clear that he wanted a political comic strip, such as Garry Trudeau's "Doonesbury" or Steve Bell's "If...". I compromised with him: half the time the comic strip would cover local politics and the rest of the time it would still be boy-meets-girl and the usual Hong Kong litter, louts and pollution jokes.

John Dux was (still is, I assume) a real character, a large, boisterous blunt-speaking Australian whom I got along with extremely well. He coaxed and wheedled me into becoming more and more outspoken in my political commentary. "Make it meaner! Make it nastier!" were his thoughtful words of advice.

I was surprised, then, when in mid-May of 1988 he called me into his office and "suggested" that I go easier on China. I was used to his challenges. From time to time he expressed complete disagreement with a cartoon. He would engage me in a mini-debate, and when he was satisfied that I could honestly and sincerely defend my position, he let the cartoon run unaltered. This anyway is an editor's duty: to make certain that controversial statements are not made just for shock value or for a cheap laugh.

But when he told me that the cartoon on the previous page could not be printed, I knew something else was up.

"We can't use words like *corrupt* to describe China," he told me. "And how can we call it *inhumane,* when it's a given *fact* that Hong Kong will be returned to China?" It wasn't the message that bothered him, but the *adjectives.* I lost the mini-debate that day. Below is how the cartoon looked in the newspaper on May 16, 1988.

It was a warning. The following week's cartoons dealt with the subject of pro-China, anti-democracy business people in Hong Kong. I phoned the editor twice that week to clear my adjectives before the drawings were completed.

On May 27, 1988, I was again summoned to the editor's office. The cartoon I had completed for

the following Monday, May 30, had to be changed. What could possibly be wrong with this one, I wondered? It's safe, it's about pollution, and it's very very true!

"Can't you think of an adjective other than *bloody* in the last panel?" John Dux asked me.

"But what's wrong with that?" I asked. "It's not an obscenity."

"Right," he replied. "I know what it means. And you know what it means." He paused. "But this newspaper is read by very many people in Beijing, people who don't have English as a native language. And they might think we mean *bloodthirsty.*"

Together we attempted to come up with an alternative word. Omitting the modifier and saying "...leave it for the Chinese to deal with," didn't have the same impact as a punchline. "The *darn* Chinese"...? (we couldn't use *damned*, of course). "The *ruddy* Chinese"...? "The *f***ing* Chinese"...? (Hmm... No, might violate China's one-child policy.) Finally he agreed with me that no other word sounded natural enough or delivered the punchline as well, so he reluctantly allowed the cartoon to go as-is.

It was my turn to challenge him. For the past several weeks I had been told to tone down the China adjectives. And now, in an otherwise innocuous cartoon, even a harmless oath was considered dangerous enough for the editor to spend half an hour of his time worrying about it. Was this the same editor who had told me "make it meaner, make it nastier"?

"This doesn't sound like your words," I told him. "It sounds like somebody else has ordered you to pass this message down to me." Perhaps Mr. Rupert Murdoch, the paper's owner, who had growing business ties with China?

He leaned slowly back in his armchair, linked his hands behind his head, and smiled.

A few months later I was again in trouble with the *South China Morning Post*. This time it wasn't about Hong Kong or China politics, but about office politics. In October 1987 there was a world-wide stock market crash...er, I mean *correction*. At the first word of a tumble in New York, the Hong Kong Stock Exchange was shut down at the order of the then-director, Ronald Li, in a misguided attempt to avoid the storm. In the summer of the following year, there were major concerns in Hong Kong about safety in the event of an emergency at the Daya Bay nuclear power plant under construction just across the border. I did a cartoon which suggested that someone with such quick shut-down reflexes as Ronald Li would be a natural safety director at the plant.

I was informed in no uncertain terms that this cartoon could not appear. Unbeknownst to me, the *South China*

Morning Post had been sued for slander by Ronald Li. The newspaper's management and lawyers were afraid that the cartoon would be held up as evidence of a "conspiracy" against Mr. Li by the *South China Morning Post*. The hastily-written alternative below appeared on August 27, 1988.

   With a change in editor came a change in concerns. Phillip Crawley, a kind-hearted and soft-spoken man, nevertheless was quite strict when it came to male body parts. He did not want to run the cartoon you see below.

   He considered the first panel to be lewd and, perhaps, juvenile. On the other hand, he admitted that he enjoyed this particular cartoon very much, and he implored me to come up with an alternative

beginning. Once again I engaged in a mini-debate with an editor and a mutual groping for alternatives. But this was no adjective problem. This was a matter of content: without the first panel, the cartoon would make no sense. The editor acknowledged this and, once again, on November 26, 1988, an editor at the *South China Morning Post* ran one of my cartoons against his own better judgement.

Ironically, the most blatant act of censoring a "Lily Wong" cartoon under political pressure had nothing to do with China, but with France! Following a holiday in Europe, I was naturally inspired to have Lily Wong and brother Rudy go there themselves.

Has anyone ever gone to Paris and actually *seen* the buildings and other sights? I never have. That is, I was in Paris for four days and the entire time my eyes were fixed firmly downward to the pavement to avoid stepping in the ubiquitous, copious, nauseating dog droppings.

The cartoon on the next page and another one along similar lines were at first approved by Phillip Crawley. Late on April 23, 1989, the night before the cartoon was meant to appear, I received a phone call at home: I had to quickly come up with alternatives to both.

Was it the off-colour subject of dog doo that was the problem? No, no, that was fine, the editor told me. But, he explained, the Consul-General of France was a testy sort of *homme* who reacted with red-cheeked outrage any time an article appeared that was in any way less than laudatory of his country. The editor was tired of receiving fiery Gallic-accented telephone calls. He just did not want to stir up His Excellency again.

"You mean you don't want to run my cartoons because you're afraid of an angry phone call?"

Not exactly. Just that week Paris had won a European award as the "cleanest city" on that continent. The *South China Morning Post* had reported the honour. My cartoons so totally contradicted this, that it wouldn't be...well...*factual.*

"Have you actually been to Paris recently?" he asked.

"Yes, just a couple months ago." And unless some miracle had occurred in the interval, Paris was the biggest open canine toilet I'd ever seen anywhere on earth, with the possible exception of Brussels. A cleanliness award didn't make sense. My cartoons did. But they were never printed.

If dog poop was proper but politically risky, then tanks crushing civilians was politically acceptable but improper.

On June 4, 1989, the tanks invaded Tiananmen Square. It was a wake-up call to Hong Kong. And a catharsis for critics. Suddenly there was no more talk of improper adjectives. We could say and draw anything we wanted about the brutal regime in China. Well, almost. During the 1990 Asian Games, held in Beijing, I suggested a few indigenous Asian sports to be added to the line-up:

IT'S DAY 3 OF THE ASIAN GAMES. WHAT EVENTS ARE LINED UP TODAY, FRED? TODAY IS "SPECIAL EVENTS" DAY.

WE'RE JUST FINISHING THE FIRST ROUND OF "BACKBENCH BRAWL", WITH THE PARLIAMENTARY TEAMS FROM TAIWAN AND SOUTH KOREA LITERALLY NECK-AND-NECK.

WE SWITCH NOW "LIVE" TO THE "CIVILIAN SLAUGHTER" PLAYOFFS, WITH THE TOP-RATED KHMER ROUGE FACING A STRONG CHALLENGE FROM THE HOME TEAM HERE IN BEIJING.

SO WHO WINS? THE ONE WITH THE HIGHEST TALLY? NO, THE ONE WHO LIES ABOUT THE LOWEST.

The editor sent it back, saying that "Civilian Slaughter" was crude and unfunny. I changed it to "Counter-Revolutionary Cricket", which at least was alliterative. But that didn't help. On September 26, 1990, the *Post's* weather report was expanded to cover the space where the cartoon would have appeared. The editor explained that the graphic image of tanks running over people was tasteless. He was probably right. But, then, it's difficult to be tasteful when commenting on anything coming out of China nowadays.

Matters of taste were also the stated reason for cancelling a cartoon featuring a delirious Deng Xiaoping. In August 1993 the weather report again took over where a cartoon would have appeared. It was a well-known fact that Deng Xiaoping was so old and enfeebled and his speech so slurred that he could only be understood by his daughter, who acted as his "interpreter". Unconfirmed reports asserted that he had developed a tendency to drool.

12

Thus my cartoon stuck by Deng's own adage of "seeking the truth from facts."

Nevertheless, David Armstrong, who had taken over the editor's position just a few weeks earlier, removed the cartoon from that day's edition without asking for a replacement. He explained that he considered the cartoon in poor taste. He assured me that the cartoon had not been cancelled for political reasons. I took him at his word.

When tycoon Robert Kuok bought a controlling interest in the *South China Morning Post*, many people were worried. Mr. Kuok has numerous business dealings in China and has openly spoken in praise of the Chinese Communist Party. Yet fears of a polar shift in the Post's editorial policy were not borne out. Mr. Kuok is an astute businessman, and obviously understood that a mildly critical editorial policy toward Beijing, such as the *Post* maintained, sells newspapers. And this being Hong Kong, money is eternally more important than principles. Nevertheless fears remained that Beijing, where principle — or rather, power — is more important than all else, might eventually exert subtle pressure on its friend Mr. Kuok.

During the week of May 15-20, 1995, "Lily Wong" dealt with the subject of the bodily organs of executed Chinese prisoners being sold for transplant operations in Hong Kong and overseas (the cartoons appear on pages 116-118).

The cartoon on Friday, May 19, 1995, described Chinese Premier Li Peng as a "fascist murderous dog." At 8:05 that evening I received a fax from editor David Armstrong that "The World of Lily Wong" was being terminated with immediate effect.

The cartoons for the following week had already been submitted and entered into the newspaper's page layout system. And yet on Monday May 22, 1995, none of the six cartoons appeared. The weather report again took their place, this time for good. "The World of Lily Wong" was finished, without even an explanation to readers.

The cartoons that should have appeared can be found on pages 121-123. Six other cartoons that were near completion at the time are also reprinted at the end.

The editor insists that the termination of "The World of Lily Wong" was a cost-cutting measure made necessary by a simultaneous rise in newsprint paper and a drop in advertising revenue. There was, he said, nothing political or sinister about the decision.

And yet this explanation has not satisfied a great many people. The *South China Morning Post* remains the single most profitable independent daily newspaper in the world. Besides, if budget was the sole reason for terminating the feature, then why were six cartoons that were already submitted and paid for tossed into the rubbish? I offered to take a substantial reduction in pay, effective immediately, in order to continue the feature. This was rejected even before I could mention a figure. Furthermore, the *South China Morning Post* was contractually obliged to give 30 days' notice of termination. I was still to be paid in full for another month following that Friday evening fax. I requested, then begged (I was upset, mind you) to be allowed to work during that time. After all, they were paying for it anyway, and I was prepared to give them their money's worth. After nine years, eight of them with the *South China Morning Post*, Lily Wong the comic strip feature and the character herself had built up a sizeable, loyal following. I begged the editor to let Lily take a final bow, wind up the story and say goodbye. I was told this was impossible.

Allegations of political censorship flew around the world. Scores of newspapers, magazines, wire services and radio stations from four continents latched on to the story of sweet, lovely Lily Wong allegedly losing her life to the dark forces of political repression. The story took on a life of its own. *Der Spiegel*, the German news magazine, reported that the paper's owner "pro-China magnate" Robert Kuok had personally ordered the strip's termination. The *Southam News* (Ontario, Canada) went further, implying a connection between the cartoon's demise and the simultaneous visit of top Chinese official Lu Ping (a fluent reader of English) to Hong Kong. Lily's image appeared in countless publications throughout Asia, Britain, continental Europe, North America, and Australia (in many cases without permission and without royalties). Like many a rock-and-roll star before her, Lily's greatest fame and success came with her demise.

Lily Wong was a well-known and popular figure in Hong Kong and abroad. She — not her creator — was interviewed numerous times by local news media, including an interview in full animation on TVB. A Broadway producer wrote a musical comedy about her, and an excerpt, complete with original songs and music, was performed once in New York (alas, he couldn't find enough investors). One New Zealander named his boat after her. When she became a mother, congratulations and baby gifts poured in. And she was the subject of countless indecent propositions by men whose wives should never live to find out. This is to say that people believed in her as a living, breathing human being.

And what would Lily have said or done if she had been allowed to say goodbye? Lily loved Hong Kong. Hong Kong was her home; she never wished to leave. Maybe she would have walked off coughing into the red, pollution-tinged sunset, or have been engulfed at the harbour front by an excrement-and-plastic-bag-saturated wave. More likely, she would have boarded an eastbound tram and, just before it disappeared out of sight into the human-and-neon-choked depths of Wanchai, she would have turned around, smiled sadly, waved and said:

"I only regret I won't be here to see the transition in 1997. I wish my beloved Hong Kong a sweeter fate than my own."

Lantau Island
Hong Kong
June 1995

15

SELECTED CARTOONS
1993-1995

All cartoons in this section appeared in the *South China Morning Post* between February 1993 and May 1995.

LILY, YOU'RE NOT SO BIG YET. LET'S GO AWAY SOMEWHERE BEFORE THE BABY COMES.

BABY CARE

TRAVEL

THIS COULD BE OUR LAST CHANCE FOR YEARS TO HAVE A ROMANTIC HOLIDAY ALONE TOGETHER!

WHAT ARE YOU TALKING ABOUT "ALONE", GWAILO??

TAHITI

Maui

LET'S TRY ONE OF THESE TRAVEL AGENCIES THAT CATER TO EXPATS.

Avon TRAVEL

EASTER HOME LEAVE PACKAGE $100,000

SUMM HOM LEAVE PACKA $90,000

PERHAPS YOU'LL LIKE OUR EXOTIC BALI "GO NATIVE" PACKAGE: FLY FIRST CLASS TO DENPASAR, TRANSFER BY CHAUFFERED MERCEDES TO YOUR LUXURY 5-STAR RESORT HOTEL, FEAST ON THE FINEST SWISS CUISINE—

London

Rent a Rolls

WAIT A MINUTE. DON'T YOU HAVE SOMETHING JUST A TAD BIT MORE DOWN-TO-EARTH?

Manila weekend shopping getaway

WHO LET THIS LAMMA ISLAND HIPPIE IN HERE??

WE WANT TO BOOK A HOLIDAY TRIP.

SURE! WE GOT HUNDREDS OF TOURS TO CHOOSE!

HOW ABOUT OUR "EUROPEAN FAIRYTALE" TOUR ... SEE LONDON, PARIS, AMSTERDAM, BERLIN, ROME. AND THEN ON DAY TWO—

ER...DON'T YOU HAVE SOMETHING LESS HURRIED, NOT IN A GROUP, WHERE WE CAN ACTUALLY MINGLE WITH THE LOCALS?

SEE? HANG OUT WITH FOREIGNERS, YOU GET NUTTY IDEAS.

WHICH AIRLINE YOU PREFER?

HMM...SINGAPORE GIRLS ARE THE BEST-LOOKING, AND KOREAN AIR GIRLS ARE A-OK. FORGET ALL NIPPON—THEIR STEWARDESSES DRESS LIKE BOY SCOUTS!

YOU JERK! YOU'RE PICKING AN AIRLINE BY COMPARING THE WOMEN IN THEIR TV ADS?!

I'M MERELY MAKING AN INFORMED CHOICE BASED ON INFORMATION PROVIDED.

IRAN AIR — THEY WEAR VEILS, RIGHT?

20

21

WAH! FINALLY RELEASED FROM JAIL FOR SPITTING!

CHANGI PRISON

FROM NOW ON IN SINGAPORE I'M OBEYING EVERYTHING THE GOVERNMENT SAYS!

MRT

LITTER

HAVE A CHILD

HELP OUR NATION GROW

ALL TRAINS →

HEY, DOLL! HOW'D YA LIKE TO BE A GOOD CITIZEN?

NEW PAPER

FEIGN

The cartoon above was censored in Singapore. The *New Paper* reprinted it, on the condition that the first panel be changed. "People don't go to jail for spitting," the Deputy Editor explained. "The cartoon is not factually correct."

THIS EAST COAST PARK IS GORGEOUS! THE BEACH IS SPOTLESS, THE WATER ABSOLUTELY CLEAN!

YEAH. BE BACK IN A LITTLE WHILE.

PUBLIC RESTROOM

ONE HOUR LATER...

RUDY, YOU'VE BEEN IN THERE FOR AN HOUR! IS ANYTHING WRONG?

NAH.

JUST HOMESICK FOR VICTORIA HARBOUR.

FEIGN

24

LITTLE INDIA! THIS IS GREAT! THE FOOD, THE SHOPS! THERE'S ALSO AN ARAB STREET NEARBY.

CAN YOU IMAGINE IF HONG KONG HAD AREAS LIKE THIS WHERE DIFFERENT ETHNIC GROUPS GOT TOGETHER?

YEAH. THEY'D TRY TO MOVE THEM TO UNDERGROUND CAR PARKS!

SINGAPORE IS NICE, BUT I CAN'T IMAGINE LIVING IN A PLACE THAT DOESN'T HAVE FREEDOM OF EXPRESSION.

EXCUSE ME, BUT WE SINGAPOREANS ENJOY VERY WIDE-RANGING FREEDOM OF EXPRESSION.

WE CAN PRAISE THE GOVERNMENT IN ENGLISH, MANDARIN, CANTONESE, MALAY, HINDI...

25

WELCOME ABOARD FLIGHT 008 TO HONG—

THIS IS A HIJACK! TAKE THIS PLANE TO CANTON!

NO WAY, JOSÉ!

RUDY! HE HAD A GUN! YOU RISKED YOUR LIFE!!

HMF. AIN'T AS BIG A RISK AS GETTING POKED FOR AN HIV TEST IF WE LANDED IN CHINA!

IT'S NICE TO BE BACK IN HONG KONG.

SINGAPORE WAS NICE, BUT THERE YOU DON'T HAVE THE RIGHT TO CRITICISE THE GOVERNMENT.

WHEREAS IN HONG KONG, NOT ONLY DOES THE GOVERNMENT GIVE YOU THE RIGHT TO CRITICISE...

THEY ALSO GIVE YOU THOUSANDS OF REASONS TO EXERCISE THAT RIGHT!

26

YOU'RE USING A COMPUTER?? FOR WHAT? MARK 6?

I'M WRITING A BOOK.

I'VE MADE A DISCOVERY THAT'LL RE-INVENT CHINA-U.S. RELATIONS, SHOCK THE WORLD AND MAKE ME **STINKING RICH!**

IS IT ABOUT FORCED PRISON LABOUR OR THE NEW "PREVENT INFERIOR CHILDREN" POLICY?

EVEN MORE SIGNIFICANT.

DENG is ELVIS!

THE SHOCKING TRUTH

COMING TO YOUR LOCAL BOOKSHOP

SEIGN

RUDY CLAIMS THAT DENG IS REALLY ELVIS PRESLEY???

SHHH! DON'T WANT THE "SUN" TO FIND OUT!

LOOK AT THE FACTS— FOR INSTANCE: WHEN WAS DENG PURGED?

1966.

AND WHEN WAS ELVIS'S BIG "COMEBACK" TV SPECIAL?

1968.

WHEN WAS ELVIS'S FINAL #1 ALBUM?

AND WHEN DID DENG FIRST RE-EMERGE TO POWER?

"ALOHA FROM HAWAII"– 1973.

1973!

AND WHEN DID ELVIS SO-CALLED "DIE"... AND DENG MAKE HIS FINAL COMEBACK AS SUPREME LEADER?

BOTH IN '77!! MY GOD! IT'S TRUE!!

SEIGN

Panel 1: "BACK IN CHINA, MAO GOT ALL THE GIRLS. BUT NOW IT WAS FINALLY **ME** SWARMING WITH CHICKS!"

BABY, WON'T YOU BE... MY PANDA BEAR

OOOH, ELVIS! UH, WHAT'S A PANDA?

Panel 2: "WITH A STRING OF HITS IN '56 AND '57, I WAS TRULY THE-- THE--"

'PARAMOUNT LEADER' OF ROCK-N-ROLL!

MM. NOT QUITE.

Panel 3: THE 'GREAT HELMSMAN' OF ROCK-N-ROLL...?

THE 'CHIEF POLITBURO MEMBER' OF ROCK-N-ROLL...?

THE 'STALINIST DICTATOR' OF--

Panel 4: HOW ABOUT 'THE KING' OF ROCK-N-ROLL?

A BIT REACTIONARY. BUT AS LONG AS IT CATCHES MICE...

FEIGN

Panel 5: DENG RECALLS...

I KNEW I'D MADE IT AS 'THE KING' WHEN I GOT ON THE ED SULLIVAN SHOW!

ptui!

Panel 6: THEY ONLY SHOWED ME FROM THE WAIST UP!

BECAUSE OF YOUR UNBRIDLED PELVIC CONTORTIONS.

Panel 7: HA! THAT'S THE HYPE MY MANAGER PUT OUT! THE REAL REASON WAS...

Panel 8: "MY NEW PLATFORM BOOTS WERE KILLING ME!"

FEIGN

I WAS ELVIS—**THE KING!** I HAD IT ALL—MONEY, FAME, GIRLS. BUT WHAT I WANTED WAS **POWER!**

I COLLECTED POLICE BADGES. BUT I WANTED TO BE THE REAL THING. I ASKED NIXON TO MAKE ME A FEDERAL MARSHAL. JUST A MARSHAL!! BUT HE SAID **NO!** *

*TRUE! (ABOUT ELVIS)

THEN HE TOLD ME HE'S GOING TO CHINA TO KISS UP TO THAT BASTARD MAO! THAT DID IT! IT WAS THE FINAL STRAW!

YOU MEAN... IF NIXON HAD MADE YOU A MARSHAL, ALL THOSE KIDS IN TIANANMEN SQUARE WOULD BE ALIVE TODAY?

MM. BUT MEMPHIS TRAFFIC OFFENDERS WATCH OUT!

FEIGN

WORD LEAKS OUT...

NATIONAL INQUISITOR

ELVIS IS ALIVE!
...and dictator of China

Michael Jackson molested me, says teen alien from Uranus.

WOMAN GIVES BIRTH TO BABY DINOSAUR

page 3

CHINESE RESTAURANTS BECOME THE RAGE ACROSS AMERICA...

LOOK! HE COULD BE BOBBY DARIN!

WONDER IF THAT'S JAMES DEAN?

GRACELAND IS REMODELED...

Welcome to GLACERAND

AND A NEW INDUSTRY IS BORN!

· FIRST · NATIONAL · **DENG IMPERSONATORS** CONTEST ·

GOTTA HUNKA HUNKA BURNIN' LEAD

DANCIN' TO THE RE-EDUCATION CENTRE ROCK

FEIGN

THE NEWS REACHES THE WHITE HOUSE...

H'LO? THAT YOU, DENGY BOY? ...OR SHOULD AH SAY 'THE KING'?

DENG IS ELVIS

NOW, BUDDY, AS ONE GOOD-OL'-BOY TO ANOTHER, AH TELL YA—Y'ALL GOT TO CANCEL THIS POLICY TO "PREVENT INFERIOR CHILDREN".

IT'S REPUGNANT AN' A TRAVESTY AGAINST ALL HUMANITY!

HEY, SO WAS MY COVER OF "BRIDGE OVER TROUBLED WATER", BUT THAT DIDN'T STOP THE STANDING OVATIONS IN VEGAS!

NOW LISTEN UP, CLINTON! I AM ELVIS! IF YOU DON'T WANT TO LOSE MILLIONS OF MY FANS' VOTES IN '96, YOU DO AS I SAY!

FIRST: UNCONDITIONAL MFN. TWO: ELVIS'S BACK ROYALTIES SINCE 1977 PAID TO MY SON'S HONG KONG BANK ACCOUNT.

AND GRACELAND TO BE "REUNITED" WITH THE MOTHERLAND!

YEAH? WELL, WHAT DO WE GET IN RETURN?

HAVE I GOT OUT-TAKES! ME 'N LITTLE RICHARD DOING "TUTTI FRUTTI", "SPINOUT" IN SWEDISH...

QUICK! TELL PAKISTAN THEY CAN BUY THOSE CHINESE MISSILES!

FEIGN

31

COMRADE DENG! YOU'RE NOT THE ONLY TYRANT CLAIMING TO BE A DEAD POP STAR!

MUAMMAR KHADAFY CLAIMS TO BE RICKY NELSON.

SADDAM HUSSEIN SAYS HE'S MARVIN GAYE.

People's Daily

AND SLOBODAN MILOSEVIC CLAIMS TO BE JANIS JOPLIN!

WHAT DO YOU SAY TO THAT?

THINK OF THE JAM SESSION WE'D HAVE!

WE RULE THE WORLD... WE BOMB THE CHILDREN...

FEIGN

RUDY, EVER SINCE YOU REPORTED THAT DENG XIAOPING IS ELVIS, EVERY PETTY DICTATOR ON EARTH IS CLAIMING TO BE A DEAD POP STAR!

THERE'S EVEN WAR BETWEEN SUDAN AND BURKINA FASO OVER WHICH LEADER IS REALLY NAT KING COLE!

YOU'VE GOT TO PUT A STOP TO THIS!

MM. THEN I BETTER CALL GOVERNMENT HOUSE FIRST.

MR. GOVERNOR, HE CLAIMS HE WAS ONLY JOKING — LU PING IS **NOT** A SID VICIOUS FAN!

anarchy

Sex Pistols

FEIGN

NOW, **THIS** IS TYPICAL HONG KONG!

WE'RE LEADERS IN COUNTERFEIT WATCHES, COUNTERFEIT DESIGNER CLOTHES...

COUNTERFEIT HAND BAGS, COUNTERFEIT COMPUTER SOFTWARE, AND NOW...

COUNTERFEIT LIBERALS!

NOTE: ALL MEMBERS OF THE "LIBERAL" PARTY WILL HENCEFORTH BE DRAWN AS **TOADS**.

GRANTED, TECHNICALLY THEY'RE INVERTEBRATES (HAVING NO BACKBONE). HOWEVER, MEALYBUGS AND JELLYFISH LOOK LOUSY IN SUITS.

MEANWHILE, EVERYONE ELSE WILL BE DEPICTED AS HUMAN BEINGS.

WELL, ALMOST EVERYONE...

FIRST BUSINESS: OUR PROPOSAL TO POSTPONE DISCUSSION OF THE GOVERNOR'S REFORMS. I BELIEVE WE ALL AGREE.

OF COURSE WE DON'T! THAT WOULD MEAN WE **STAND** FOR SOMETHING. SINCE WHEN DO WE STAND FOR ANYTHING??

SURE WE DO. AT LEAST, THERE'S THINGS WE **NEVER** STAND FOR, LIKE ELECTIONS.

I KNOW WHAT I **CAN'T** STAND — MARTIN LEE!

I KNOW! LET'S POSTPONE THE PROPOSAL TO POSTPONE THE PROPOSALS!

ALL IN FAVOUR SAY 'MAYBE'...

THWAP!

POSTPONING DEBATE ON POLITICAL REFORMS — ISN'T THAT THE COWARD'S WAY OUT?

NONSENSE! POSTPONEMENT IS A NOBLE ACT!

IF MOSES HAD POSTPONED PARTING THE RED SEA, HE WOULDN'T HAVE GOTTEN LOST IN THE DESERT FOR 40 YEARS!

IF TRUMAN HAD POSTPONED DROPPING THE BOMB, PEOPLE WOULDN'T HAVE LOST SO MUCH MONEY IN THE HIROSHIMA PROPERTY MARKET!

IF #@*%!%! MAJOR HAD POSTPONED APPOINTING PATTEN...

YOU'RE A TRUE VISIONARY, ALLEN TOAD!

FEIGN

OUR GUEST ON "NEWSLINE" IS "LIBERAL" PARTY CHAIRMAN MR. ALLEN TOAD.

MR. TOAD, CAN YOU EXPLAIN WHY YOU WANT TO POSTPONE DISCUSSION OF THE GOVERNOR'S POLITICAL REFORMS?

IT'S LIKE THIS (rivet)...

IF WE WANT A THROUGH TRAIN, WE MUSTN'T ROCK THE BOAT, OR THEY'LL SET UP A SECOND STOVE AND WE'LL HAVE A LAME DUCK!

NICE TO HEAR ABOUT YOUR CHILDREN'S BATH TOYS, MR. TOAD. BUT TO REPEAT THE QUESTION...

OUR NEW 'LIBERAL' PARTY NEEDS YOUR HELP. THE PUBLIC ISN'T GRASPING OUR MESSAGE.

WHICH IS...?

PINCHBECK Public Relations

WE'RE AGAINST DIRECT ELECTIONS, AND WE INTEND TO RUN FOR DIRECT ELECTION.

WE WANT INFLUENCE IN LEGCO, BUT WE DON'T WANT LEGCO TO HAVE ANY INFLUENCE.

I THINK THEY'RE DOING SOME LATERAL THINKING.

FEIGN

35

FORGET INDIRECT VERSUS DIRECT ELECTIONS! THE 'LIBERAL' PARTY HAS A RADICAL NEW APPROACH FOR POLITICAL REFORM.

PINCHBECK
Public Relations

UNDER THE OLD SYSTEM, WE USED TO SHINE GOVERNOR WILSON'S SHOES, WHO IN TURN BOWED AND SCRAPED TO OFFICIALS IN BEIJING.

WHEREAS UNDER OUR NEW SYSTEM...

WE'VE GONE FROM INDIRECT TO FULLY DIRECT KOW-TOWING!

CRC TRIP TO BEIJING

WE NEED A GENERAL DESCRIPTIVE LABEL FOR THE LIBERAL PARTY THAT WE CAN FEED TO THE PRESS.

THEY'RE NOT REALLY "LIBERALS".

"LIBERALS"

WHAT WORDS COME TO MIND WHEN YOU THINK OF THE CRC?

HMM... WAFFLERS... WINDBAGS... MONEY-BAGS...

PINCHBECK
Public Relations
Toronto · Sydney

WISHY-WASHY... GUTLESS... MEDIOCRE...

BY GEORGE, YOU'VE GOT IT!

Mr. ALLEN TOAD AND OTHER LEADING MEDIOCRATS TODAY MET WITH...

36

FUNNY HOW THERE HAVE BEEN SO MANY SHARK SIGHTINGS IN HONG KONG WATERS.

That Other Paper
GALACTIC EXCLUSIVE:
WE SPOT ANOTHER SHARK!!!
Strewth!
Trogg
Smash
SINO-BRITISH

YET YOU DON'T HEAR OF A SINGLE ONE ACROSS THE BORDER.

HM. WONDER WHY?

burrp

THIS'LL **REALLY** TEACH PATTEN!

SPIRIT OF LEI FENG

SUMMER FUN DAY AT A POPULAR HONG KONG BEACH...

GASP! NOT AGAIN! A SINISTER CRESCENT SURFACES FROM THE POLLUTED DEPTHS...

IS IT THE MURDEROUS GREY TIGER SHARK? A KILLER GREAT WHITE?

OR SOMETHING OF A MORE REDDISH HUE...?

SEE ANY UNITED DEMOCRATS YET?

DUNNO. DOES MARTIN LEE WEAR SPANDEX?

37

DO YOU SUPPORT PATTEN'S REFORMS?

HAH?!? I—I'LL SAY ANYTHING! J—JUST DON'T HURT ME!!!

TSK. I TOLD YOU HE LOOKED LIKE A LIBERAL PARTY TYPE.

COMRADES, WE KEEP UP THE SHARK ATTACKS UNTIL PATTEN DROPS HIS FILTHY PROPOSALS!

AT THE SAME TIME, YOU MAKE SURE THAT AUSTRALIAN SHARK CATCHER DOESN'T HOOK ANY SHARKS!

WHY NOT?

WE DON'T WANT SYDNEY TO GET THE PUBLICITY!

AIEEYAAA! LOOK! A **REAL SHARK!!**

HELLLP!! IT'S GOING TO RAM US! IT'S—

IT'S—**OOF!!**

NEVER LET A SHARK GIVE YOU A HICKEY.

COMRADES! IT WORKED!!

THE SHARK ATTACKS MADE HONG KONG CAPITULATE! FINALLY THEY KNOW WHO'S MASTER!

HOW DO YOU KNOW?

JUST LOOK. AT EVERY BEACH IN THE TERRITORY...

THEY'VE RAISED THE **RED FLAG!**

39

HONEY, I'M RETURNING TO WORK IN A FEW WEEKS. SHOULDN'T WE LOOK FOR AN AMAH?

BUT WE HAVE CRYSTAL'S GRAND-PARENTS LIVING RIGHT HERE. WE DON'T NEED AN AMAH!

HM. MY FATHER AGREES WITH YOU.

SEE? HE WANTS TO TAKE CARE OF HIS GRAND-DAUGHTER!

NO, HE SAYS IT'S BAD ENOUGH ALREADY HAVING ONE FOREIGNER IN THE HOUSE!

MOPS R US EMPLOYMENT AGENCY. HOW MAY I HELP YOU?

YEAH, WE'RE LOOKING FOR A LIVE-IN MAID.

I SEE. AND DO YOU PREFER FILIPINA, THAI OR SRI LANKAN?

MAIDS! MAIDS! MAIDS!

MOPS R US   566-25??

Desperate women from cholera-ridden gnat-infested jungle lands to enhance YOUR luxury lifestyle

JUST A SEC. LET ME ASK.

DO YOU LIKE CHICKEN ADOBO, TOM YAM SOUP, OR CURRIED BRINJAL?

HOW TO RAISE A CHILD GENIUS

GOOD MORNING, MA'AM. I AM ERMA.

YES, COME IN, COME IN.

SO, ERMA, UM...WHAT'S YOUR EXPERIENCE WORKING WITH CHILDREN?

MY LAST EMPLOYER HAD TWO.

GOOD. AH... HEE HEE... I DON'T KNOW WHAT ELSE TO ASK.

I DO.

WHAT'S YOUR EXPERIENCE IN DEEP TISSUE SWEDISH MASSAGES?

AND WHAT DID YOU DO IN THE PHILIPPINES BEFORE COMING TO HONG KONG?

I WORKED IN THE FISHERIES, SIR. I HAVE A MASTER'S DEGREE IN AQUACULTURE.

WOW.

HOW WOULD IT MAKE YOU FEEL, THEN, IF ONE OF YOUR EMPLOYERS ONLY FINISHED FORM 6 AND WHOSE ONLY PROFESSIONAL SKILL IS TYPING?

NOT AS BAD AS IT MAKES YOU FEEL, SIR.

FEIGN

FEIGN

WHY DIDN'T YOU RENEW YOUR PREVIOUS CONTRACT?

THEY ARE VERY CRUEL CHINESE EMPLOYERS.

THEY MAKE ME WORK IN BROTHER'S SHOP, CLEAN COUSIN'S, UNCLE'S AND IN-LAWS' FLATS, NEVER GIVE ME SUNDAYS OR HOLIDAYS AND I EAT ONLY LEFTOVERS FROM THEIR DIRTY RICEBOWLS!

I ASK YOU — WOULD YOU PUT UP WITH WORKING LIKE A SLAVE, SLEEPING ON A COLD KITCHEN FLOOR, AND ONLY TO BE PAID $1200??

FUNNY. THAT'S THE QUESTION I WAS GOING TO ASK YOU!

ONE LAST QUESTION, ERMA — DO YOU SPEAK CANTONESE?

WHY, OF COURSE, MA'AM.

ONLY AN IDIOT COULD LIVE WITH A CHINESE FAMILY FOR TWO YEARS AND NOT SPEAK THE LANGUAGE!

OOPS. SORRY, SIR.

YOU'RE HIRED!!

42

COME, MISS WONG, MR. CHIU. WE'RE TO BE PART OF THE WORKING GROUP ON POST-1997 GEOGRAPHICAL NAME CHANGES.

Hong Kong Government DEPT. of PREVARICAT... and OBFUSCATI...

THE CHINESE SIDE WILL WANT TO RENAME SUCH PLACES AS VICTORIA PEAK AND KING'S ROAD— "PEOPLE'S THIS", "PEOPLE'S THAT"...

BUT, NEVER MIND. "A ROSE BY ANY OTHER NAME WOULD SMELL AS SWEET."

OR, IN THE CASE OF VICTORIA HARBOUR...

FIRST ORDER OF BUSINESS — RENAMING THE HARBOUR.

SINO-BRITISH WORKING GROUP TO ABOLISH FILTHY COLONIAL PLACE NAMES IN THE HKSAR

DO NOT SPIT

THE HONG KONG CONTINGENT SUBMITS THAT THE HARBOUR BE NAMED AFTER COMRADE DENG XIAOPING.

BRILLIANT! CONSIDERING THAT HE IS THE ARCHITECT OF THE JOINT DECLARATION AND 'ONE COUNTRY TWO SYSTEMS'.

ACTUALLY, IT'S BECAUSE THE HARBOUR IS FULL OF LITTLE BOTTLES*!

* LITTLE BOTTLE = DENG'S NICKNAME

43

TRADITIONALLY, EVERY HONG KONG GOVERNOR HAS A LANDMARK NAMED AFTER HIM.

HM. NORMALLY YOU NAME SOMETHING ONLY AFTER THEY'RE RETIRED OR DEAD, RIGHT?

THEN WE'RE DELIGHTED TO LET YOU NAME ANYTHING YOU WANT AFTER CHRIS PATTEN.

PROVIDED YOU DO IT THIS AFTERNOON!!

OKAY, WE'VE AGREED TO RENAME EXCHANGE SQUARE AS 'SOCIALISM WITH CHINESE CHARACTERISTICS SQUARE'.

HENCEFORTH, PRINCE EDWARD WILL BE 'GREAT HELMSMAN', THE MACLEHOSE TRAIL IS 'LONG MARCH TRAIL' AND THE ROYAL JOCKEY CLUB WILL BE THE 'PEOPLE'S EQUESTRIAN COLLECTIVE'.

LAST ONE FOR TODAY— CAT STREET. WE SUGGEST 'POLITBURO STREET'.

EH? WHY POLITBURO?

BECAUSE THEY'RE BOTH FULL OF TATTERED ANTIQUES!

Genuine news item:

46

47

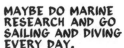

STUART, I THINK THIS BUSINESS ABOUT A MID-LIFE CRISIS IS A LOAD OF RUBBISH.

CENTRAL ASIA on a budget

SOUNDS TO ME MORE LIKE ADOLESCENT SELF-INDULGENCE. ONLY A GWAILO WOULD COME UP WITH SOMETHING LIKE THAT!

OH YEAH? MAYBE LOCAL MEN JUST EXPRESS IT A BIT DIFFERENTLY!

SIGH... I FEEL LIKE QUITTING YEN-DENOMINATED SECURITIES AND TAKING UP SOMETHING MORE MEANINGFUL — LIKE ECU'S.

? ?

FEIGN

LILY, ALL I WANT IS ONE YEAR OFF TO FINISH MY NOVEL.

SURE. OKAY. IF THAT'S WHAT YOU NEED TO DO. I'M SURE ON MY SECRETARY'S SALARY WE CAN NEARLY COVER THE RENT.

OF COURSE, YOUR DAUGHTER MIGHT HAVE TO GO WITHOUT FORMULA, BABY FOOD, CLOTHES, TOYS, NAPPIES...

SIGH... PAMPERS' GAIN, LITERATURE'S LOSS.

Pampers 72 S

FEIGN

THIS IS THE LAST STRAW! TIME TO IMPLEMENT DENG'S SPEECH AND RESUME SOVEREIGNTY EARLY!

PATTEN'S SPEECH

HONG KONG & MACAU INTIMIDATION OFFICE

COGNAC

SEND IN THE TANKS!!

B-B-BUT, COMRADE!

WHAT ABOUT WORLD OPINION? THINK OF THE CONSEQUENCES!

CONSEQUENCES?? NUMBSKULL! WE'RE NO LONGER BIDDING FOR THE OLYMPICS!

COGNAC

FEIGN

Deng Xiaoping threatened to "resume sovereignty early" in the event of "serious disturbances" (i.e. democratic reforms) in Hong Kong.

COMRADE, WE CAN'T TAKE BACK HONG KONG EARLY! DENG SAID WE'D DO THAT ONLY IF THERE WERE "SERIOUS DISTURBANCES".

HONG KONG & MACAU INTIMIDATION OFFICE

EVEN IN JUNE '89, WE DIDN'T SEND IN THE TANKS UNTIL TIANANMEN SQUARE WAS PACKED WITH TENS OF THOUSANDS OF STUDENTS!

HMM ... GOOD POINT...

LET'S WAIT TILL SUNDAY, WHEN STATUE SQUARE IS PACKED WITH TENS OF THOUSANDS OF FILIPINAS!

ASK ANY LOCAL CHINESE— THAT IS A SERIOUS DISTURBANCE.

FEIGN

51

THERE WERE WILD SCENES IN THE STREETS OF HONG KONG TODAY, AS CHINA RESUMED SOVEREIGNTY 3½ YEARS EARLY.

THIS AFTERNOON A CONVOY OF MAINLAND OFFICIALS DROVE INTO CENTRAL DISTRICT.

AS THEIR CARS PARADED BY, ONLOOKERS BROKE INTO CHEERS AND DANCING IN THE STREET.

"THOUGH NOT NECESSARILY FOR THE OFFICIALS."

LOOK! MY MERCEDES THAT WAS STOLEN LAST APRIL!

MY JAGUAR!

THE P.L.A. HAS ENTERED HONG KONG 3½ YEARS EARLY...

WE'VE GOT PATTEN. NOW, ARE THOSE ALL THE UNITED DEMOCRATS?

OH, STUART! I JUST HAD THE MOST AWFUL DREAM! THERE WERE GUNS AND THUGS AND LOOTING AND BUTCHERY!

AND THEY WERE SINGLING OUT FOREIGNERS AND—

BOO HOO HOO

FUNNY. SAME THING HAPPENED IN MY DREAM.

EXCEPT, I WAS DREAMING ABOUT BEING A TOURIST IN FLORIDA!

Local fisher people reported sighting a mermaid in Hong Kong waters.

53

WAI, EVERYBODY, I WANT YOU TO MEET MY NEW GIRLFRIEND.

SHE JUST ARRIVED IN HONG KONG.

HAH?! IS SHE CHINESE, THEN?

UH...HOW DO I PUT THIS? I THINK SHE'S HALF CHINESE AND HALF ... ER ... LET ME ASK...

MACKEREL!

SOUNDS SCOTTISH! I KNEW SHE WAS A GWAIPOH!!

SIGH... THERE USED TO BE A THRIVING MERMAID COMMUNITY IN THE SOUTH CHINA SEA.

WE MADE OUR LIVING IN THE TRADITIONAL WAY— LURING INNOCENT SAILORS TO THEIR DOOM.

BUT SADLY, THOSE DAYS ARE OVER.

WHY? WHAT HAPPENED?

WE STARTED GETTING TOO MUCH COMPETITION FROM CHINA'S PUBLIC SECURITY BUREAU!

MORE HK SHIPS SHOT AT CONFISCATED BY CHINA

FEIGN

I'VE CALLED ALL THE NEWS BUREAUS, GOT YOU A SLOT AT OCEAN PARK, A GUEST SHOT ON "E.Y.T.", EVEN PLAYBOY'S INTERESTED IN NUDE MERMAID PICS!

WE'LL MAKE A FORTUNE!

RUDY, I CAN'T. I WANT TO GO HOME.

BUT WE'LL BE RICH!!

DEAR, I HAVE ALL THE RICHES OF THE SEA.

NOT FOR LONG YOU DON'T!

DREDGING KILLING FISH

CEMENT CASTING IN LAMMA BAY

NUCLEAR WASTE IN JAPAN SEA

RUDY, COME JOIN ME UNDER THE SEA! YOU CAN PLAY THE SEAHORSES! WE'LL BE TOGETHER ALWAYS!

HEY, WHY NOT?

OH, DARLING! MMMMMMM

PFRTHWMPT!

TASTES LIKE RAW CUTTLEFISH SLIME!!

RETCH TOBACCO BREATH!!

"...AND NEVER THE TWAIN SHALL MEET..."

FEIGN

55

MY PARENTS ARRIVE THIS MORNING. LET ME CALL THE AIRLINE TO CHECK.

I'M SORRY, SIR, THAT FLIGHT HAS BEEN DELAYED INDEFINITELY. THEY'RE STUCK IN A HOLDING PATTERN OVER TOKYO.

MY GOD! WHAT'S WRONG??

NOTHING, SIR, IT'S NORMAL. REMEMBER, THIS IS AN AMERICAN CARRIER...

THIS IS GROUND CONTROL... FOR THE 28th TIME, HONG KONG IS **NOT** IN JAPAN!

LISTEN, YOU LYIN' S.O.B.! LET ME REMIND YOU AGAIN WHO WON THE WAR!

FEIGN

THIS IS WHERE SIX ADULTS AND A CHILD LIVE?? IT'S A **SHOEBOX!**

IT'S 694 SQUARE FEET, MOM — BIG FOR HONG KONG. WE CAN'T AFFORD MORE.

WHY? WHAT'S THIS CUBBY-HOLE WORTH?

IN U.S. DOLLARS, ABOUT...

Dear Agnes,
...and you should see my son's million dollar mansion. Every time you turn around – a servant!

FEIGN

56

AND THESE ARE MY PARENTS.

SO NICE TO MEET YOU, MR. AND MRS. WONG!

SO... UH... HEH-HEH...

ER...SO... HOW YA LIKE THEM TORONTO BLUE JAYS TROUNCING THE PHILLIES, HUH?

BLUE JAYS? FILLIES? WHAT'S HE TALKING ABOUT?

BIRDS AND HORSES, I THINK.

SO NICE TO SEE THEY FOUND SOMETHING IN COMMON ALREADY!

RACING FORM

A BANQUET IN OUR HONOUR! HOW THRILLING!

WHAT'S IN THE BAG?

YOU'LL SEE.

SHRIEK! THE SHRIMPS HAVE HEADS ON THEM!

YOU MEAN WE SHARE THE FOOD?!

HELP! SOMEONE PUT CHICKEN FEET ON MY PLATE!

WAITER! BRINGEE SUGAR FOR MY TEA, CHOP CHOP!

WHAT'S THIS GLOP?

SKIP THE MEAL. JUST BRING THE FORTUNE COOKIES.

I DON'T KNOW THESE PEOPLE.

GIVE ME ONE!

pfoo!

57

STUART, DARLING, WHEN ARE YOU MOVING BACK TO AMERICA?

ARE YOU KIDDING? THE ECONOMY IS A MESS! THERE ARE NO JOBS FOR SOMEONE LIKE ME.

OH, COME ON! WITH YOUR SEVEN YEARS EXPERIENCE IN TOP ASIAN AD AGENCIES, YOU COULD EASILY FIND WORK—

PUMPING GAS.

I'M AFRAID YOU NEED A PH.D. FOR THAT NOWADAYS. THOUGH THEY DO NEED PARKING LOT ATTENDANTS!

...AND REMEMBER TO PHONE YOUR SISTER ON HER ANNIVERSARY AND WHEN ARE YOU MOVING BACK TO L.A. AND IT ISN'T TOO LATE TO GET INTO LAW SCHOOL AND YOU NEED A HAIRCUT AND—

DAMN IT, MOM! WILL YOU SHUT UP WITH THE GOD DAMN NAGGING ALREADY?!!

KABONK!

NO **CHINESE** BOY TALKING TO MUMMY LIKE THAT!

HONEY, YOU DID IT! YOU FINALLY BROKE THE ICE BETWEEN THEM!

LOOK AT THOSE POOR PEOPLE IN BOSNIA.

SURROUNDED BY ETHNIC HATRED, INNOCENT PEOPLE BEING GUNNED DOWN IN BROAD DAYLIGHT!

CHILDREN DODGING BULLETS, NEIGHBOURS KILLING EACH OTHER! ≧SOB!≦ CAN YOU IMAGINE LIVING LIKE THAT??

YOU FORGET, WE'RE FROM LOS ANGELES.

STUART, WHAT ARE YOU DOING WITH YOUR LIFE HERE IN CRAZY HONG KONG?

YOU COULD MOVE BACK TO AMERICA WHERE YOU BELONG! LIVE IN A REAL HOUSE, WITH A YARD! MAYBE EVEN GO BACK TO SCHOOL, STUDY MEDICINE...

AND THINK OF YOUR DAUGHTER — HOW GREAT IF SHE COULD GROW UP RIGHT NEXT DOOR TO HER PATERNAL GRANDPARENTS...

MOM, GO TO BED.

JUST TRYING TO HELP, DEAR.

SO, HAVE WE PACKED EVERYTHING? THE FAKE CHANEL HANDBAGS, THE COPY ROLEXES...

THE COUNTERFEIT FILA JACKETS, FAKE YVES SAINT LAURENT POLO SHIRTS AND GUCCI BELTS AND SCARVES...

THE FAKE "100% SILK" NECKTIES, COUNTERFEIT GARFIELD T-SHIRTS...

THE ILLICIT SOFTWARE, BOOTLEG MICHAEL JACKSON CD'S FOR MELANIE...

HONG KONG IS A GENUINE SHOPPER'S PARADISE!

HOW WOULD YOU KNOW?

YOU MUST BE GLAD WE'RE GOING.

NO, I WANT **ANOTHER** TWO WEEKS OF BEING NAGGED TO DEATH!

CAT PACIF
Flt. 0

AND I'VE HAD ENOUGH WHINING AND BELLY-ACHING ABOUT CROWDS AND NOISE AND THE FOOD TO LAST ME TWO **YEARS**!!

"CUT YOUR HAIR!" "WEAR BETTER SUITS!" "GO TO LAW SCHOOL!" WHEW! THANK GOD YOU'LL BE 6000 MILES FROM—

STUART, AREN'T YOU GOING TO SAY GOODBYE TO YOUR PARENTS?

HUH? OH...SORRY. I'M JUST SO EMOTIONAL TO SEE YOU GO...

CATHA
Flt. 0

A well-known luxury residential high-rise placed signs in the elevators, ordering dogs and Filipina maids to use the service lifts.

61

EXCUSE ME, I'M A RESIDENT OF THIS BUILDING.

ESTATE MANAGEMENT

I'M OUTRAGED THAT YOU WOULD BAN A CERTAIN RACE OF PEOPLE FROM THE LIFTS!

AND WHAT'S MORE, COMPARING THEM TO DOGS!

HE'S RIGHT. IT IS UNFAIR.

SOME OF THEM PEDIGREE BREEDS ARE WORTH MORE THAN A MAID GETS IN 3 YEARS!

FEIGN

IN THIS DAY AND AGE, YOU WOULDN'T EXPECT TO FIND NOTICES LIKE THIS IN FANCY UP-MARKET HIGH-RISES.

NO DOGS

NO FILIPINAS

WHY NOT? THEY HAVE TO LIVE UP TO THEIR IMAGE.

NO DOGS

NO FILIPIN

NO DOGS

NO FILIPINAS

THESE BUILDINGS ALL ADVERTISE THEMSELVES AS "LUXURY LIFESTYLE APARTMENTS...

NO SMOKING

...FOR DISCRIMINATING PEOPLE."

FEIGN

62

ALL RIGHT, ERMA, LET'S GO.

🚫 NO DOGS
🚫 NO FILIPINAS

WAI! YOU! CAN'T YOU READ THE SIGN?!

BE BRAVE, ERMA. REMEMBER ROSA PARKS IN MONTGOMERY, ALABAMA, WHO REFUSED TO SIT IN THE BACK OF THE BUS, AND SPARKED OFF THE GREAT CIVIL RIGHTS MOVEMENT OF THE 1960'S!

FORGET IT, THEN!

SHE NEVER MADE A CENT OFF THE MOVIE RIGHTS!

YOU'VE BEEN IN HONG KONG TOO LONG.

WAH! THE STUPID ENGLISH NEWSPAPERS ARE ON OUR BACKS.

ESTATE MANAGEMENT

WE GOT PROTESTORS OUTSIDE THE BUILDING.

We are not HOUSEPETS

HALT RACISM TOWARD FILIPINOS

ALL RIGHT! THEY WIN! TEAR DOWN THE SIGN!

🚫 NO DOGS
🚫 NO FILIPINAS

WE'RE NOT COMPARING THEM TO DOGS ANY MORE. NOW WHAT DO THEY WANT??

We are not HOUSEPETS

🚫 NO FILIPINAS

🚫 NO DOGS

63

WAH! PEOPLE ARE MAKING ZILLIONS IN PROPERTY SPECULATION. WE OUGHTA GET IN ON IT!

ISN'T IT TOO LATE? A MARKET THIS CRAZY COULD CRASH ANY DAY!

NAH. I GOT IT FIGURED.

WE BUY IN NORTH LANTAU. THEN IF IT DOES CRASH...

WE CALL IT "AIRPORT-RELATED" AND THE GOVERNMENT WILL INJECT $60 BILLION!

ISN'T THERE SOMETHING ... ER ... MORALLY REPUGNANT ABOUT PROPERTY SPECULATION?

YOU CREATE NOTHING, PROVIDE NO SERVICE, MAKE NO CONTRIBUTION WHATSOEVER TO SOCIETY OR THE WORLD, AND YET MAKE OBSCENE PROFITS OUT OF IT!

THAT'S THE BEAUTY OF IT, GWAILO.

IF MORE PEOPLE MADE A LIVING BY CREATING NOTHING, THIS WORLD WOULD BE A BETTER PLACE!

64

HERE'S A FLAT IN YOUR PRICE RANGE: 512 SQ FT, LOW FLOOR, IMAGINARY SEA VIEW...

GREAT. WHEN CAN WE LOOK AT IT?

HAH??

HEY, WE'RE ABOUT TO SPEND $5 MILLION! OF COURSE WE NEED TO SEE IT FIRST!

I HATE #∴%!@!!∴Ḟ END-USERS...

FORTUNA Fashions & Property

NO TRYING GOODS
No Exchange

FORTUNA Fashions & Property Boutique

OKAY, WE'LL BUY THIS PLACE. LET'S TALK PRICE.

NO TALK PRICE. YOU PAY MARKET RATE. WHILE WE TALK, PRICE GO UP BY THE MINUTE.

BY THE MINUTE? OH, COME ON!

HONG KONG TELEPHONE TIME 11:43 ... PROPERTY PRICES $9850 PER SQUARE FOOT -click-

FEIGN

65

HERE IT IS— OUR INVESTMENT PROPERTY!

WAH! TH—THERE'S PEOPLE LIVING HERE!

GOD! RENTERS MUST **REALLY** BE SCREWED BY ALL THIS PROPERTY SPECULATION FEVER!

NO, IT'S GREAT!

WITH A NEW OWNER EVERY TEN DAYS, WE LOST TRACK YEARS AGO OF WHO TO SEND A RENT CHEQUE TO!

WAI! WE JUST SOLD OUR INVESTMENT PROPERTY FOR AN $800,000 PROFIT!!

LET'S BUY A RACE HORSE!

A BMW!

IT WAS FAST, UNEARNED MONEY. MY SHARE GOES TO A CHARITY FOR NEEDY ORPHANS.

WHAT'D YOU EVER SEE IN HER?

HEY, SHE LOOKED GOOD IN BLUEJEANS.

66

WE NEED ADVICE ON HOW TO INVEST $800,000.

Samolians Ltd. FINANCIAL ADVISORS

$800,000...? MM ... THAT LEAVES YOU... $520,000 TO INVEST.

WHAT ARE YOU TALKING ABOUT?

WE SET ASIDE 15% FOR TAXES. AND THIS BEING HONG KONG, ANOTHER 20%...

TO BUY LUXURY ITEMS TO SHOW OFF HOW MUCH MONEY YOU HAVE!

WE'RE STRONGLY RECOMMENDING LAMPBLACK FUTURES— CHIEF INGREDIENT IN DRAWING INK.

Samolians Ltd. FINANCIAL ADVISORS

WITH MORE AND MORE ASIANS APPEARING IN COMICS AND EDITORIAL CARTOONS, VAST QUANTITIES OF INK ARE BEING CONSUMED JUST TO BLACKEN THEIR HAIR!

WAH! WHAT ABOUT INVESTING IN OTHER COLOURS AS WELL?

TOO LATE.

THE NEW AIRPORT HAS ALREADY CORNERED THE MARKET IN RED INK!

FEIGN

FEIGN

67

WAH! HERE'S THE JOB FOR ME!

"CHINA REPORTER FOR HONG KONG NEWSPAPER. NO EXPERIENCE NECESSARY."

"MUST HAVE PASSABLE PUTONGHUA, GOOD WRITTEN CHINESE"

"AND CHANGES OF UNDERWEAR FOR TWELVE YEARS."

Hong Kong journalist Xi Yang was jailed in China for 12 years for "revealing state secrets" after publishing an article about foreign exchange rates.

I'M HERE TO APPLY AS A CHINA NEWS REPORTER.

MM. FILL OUT THIS FORM.

HAH? WHAT'S THIS ABOUT?

OTHER SKILLS
page 2
✓ check one
☐ GARDENING
☐ MINEROLOGY
☐ SEWING
☐ CARPENTRY
☐ CERAMICS

IT HELPS US DETERMINE YOUR SPECIALTY AREA OF REPORTING.

GARDEN-ING??

SURE. IF YOU'RE AN ECONOMIC REPORTER, THEY'LL SENTENCE YOU TO A TEA FARM LABOUR CAMP; POLITICAL REPORTERS GO TO THE SALT MINES; COURT REPORTERS SEW JEANS...

RUDY IS IN BEIJING...

THIS IS THE LIFE! A FOREIGN CORRESPONDENT IN CHINA!

PWEET! STOP RIGHT THERE, LYING FOREIGN PROPAGANDIST!

PWEET! OKAY, YOU CAN GO AGAIN!

PUBLIC SECURITY BUREAU TAILS CHANGING SHIFT.

The cartoon below is based on a joke I heard in Poland:

I'M DOING A STORY ON CHINESE BANKS. IF I DEPOSIT 1000 YUAN, HOW WOULD I KNOW IT'S SAFE?

PEOPLE'S BANK OF CHINA

IT'S GUARANTEED BY THE BANK.

WHAT IF THE BANK FAILS?

THEN IT'S BACKED BY THE CHINESE GOVERNMENT AND THE COMMUNIST PARTY.

YEAH, AND WHAT IF THE COMMUNISTS ARE OVERTHROWN?

HELL, MISTER! YOU'D BEGRUDGE 1000 YUAN FOR THAT?!

69

NEW PRISONERS, YOU WILL REPORT TO THE FOLLOWING WORK UNITS!

BEIJING No.7 RE-EDUCATION CAMP & SOFT TOYS FACTORY

YOU! COOKIE MONSTER PUPPETS! YOU, YOU AND YOU! NERF BALLS! AND YOU WITH THE LIPS! CAT TOYS!

CAT TOYS?!

HEY, COUNT YOURSELF LUCKY.

THE WORST OFFENDERS ARE STUCK IN SOLITARY WITH BARNEY THE DINOSAUR!

B Block

NOO! AAAAH! SHOOT ME INSTEAD!

FEIGN

BLEH. THIS SUCKS! THE NEXT TWENTY YEARS MAKING CAT TOYS.

CATNIP

I BEEN HERE SINCE '83. AIN'T SO BAD. THE CATNIP KEEPS YOU MELLOW.

WELL, I'M GETTING OUT!

CAT

GUY TRIED THAT BACK IN... OH, '91. SEWED HIMSELF INSIDE A GIANT CATNIP MOUSE.

AND?

HE WAS EXPORTED TO THE LION'S DEN AT THE CHICAGO ZOO!

CA

FEIGN

AT THE WASHINGTON HOME OF SOCKS THE CAT...

HERE, SOCKSIE-POO!

BABY, I GOT YOU A NEW CATNIP MOUSE TO PLAY—

OOPS, WHAT'S THAT?

GASP!

To HooM iT MAY CONCERN— HELP! I'S STUCK iN A CHINESE PRISON FAKTORY FOR CALLiNG Li PENG A BUTHEAD. GET ME OUT! YERS TROOLY, Rudy Wong M.Y. #03873-089

DADDY! SOCKS WANTS YOU TO CANCEL MFN!

GOOD IDEAR. FOR ONCE, NO ONE COULD ACCUSE HILLARY OF MAKIN' POLICY!

LADIES AND GENTLEMEN, THE PRESIDENT OF THE UNITED STATES.

CNN

HOWDY. THIS MORNING MAH CAT SOCKS DISCOVERED YET ANOTHER POLITICAL PRISONER IN CHINA, A MISTER RUDY WONG, JAILED FER HIS BELIEFS. AH SAY, AMERICA'S PATIENCE IS RUN OUT!

AH HAVE HERE TH' BILL FOR RENEWAL OF CHINA'S MFN. NOW, UNLESS MISTER WONG IS RELEASED WITHIN 48 HOURS...

MFN: China

SOCKS HERE WILL DO TO THIS HERE PAPER WHAT HE DONE ALREADY TO TH' OVAL OFFICE CURTAINS!

KILL THAT CAT!!

MFN

FEIGN

72

BOTHER! IT'S UP TO OUR DEPARTMENT TO DO SOMETHING ABOUT THIS CHOLERA EPIDEMIC.

Dept. of Prevarication and Obfuscation

WHY US?

IN   PENDING

GOVERNMENT, MISS WONG, IS LIKE A GAME OF "HOT POTATO".

FIRST THERE'S A CHOLERA OUTBREAK.

EPD PUSHES THE POTATO TO URBAN SERVICES. THEY PASS IT TO HEALTH. HEALTH DUMPS IT ON AG AND FISH. AG AND FISH PASSES TO US.

Dept. of Prevarication and Obfuscation

THEN -DING!- SOMEBODY DIES AND WE'RE OUT!

IN   PEN

A cholera outbreak was traced to highly polluted sea water from Aberdeen Harbour being used to store live fish in local seafood restaurants.

HAS IT OCCURRED TO ANYONE THAT THIS SEAFOOD CHOLERA EPIDEMIC ERUPTED ONLY...

YAWN...

Dept. of Prevarication and Obfuscation

AFTER THE GOVERNMENT CRACKED DOWN ON ILLEGAL DUMPING OF MEDICAL WASTES AT SEA?

SEEMS THE VACCINES AND ANTIBIOTICS LEFT IN ALL THOSE USED SYRINGES WERE KEEPING LOCAL MARINE LIFE DISEASE-FREE!

I FOUND IT IN THE PARK. IT'S TO KEEP HIM HEALTHY.

74

THIS REPORT SUGGESTS THAT ULTRAVIOLET LIGHTS PLACED OVER FISH TANKS WILL KILL ALL THE HARMFUL BACTERIA AND—

THAT'S IT! WE NEED ULTRAVIOLET LIGHT TO STERILISE ABERDEEN HARBOUR!

WHERE DO WE FIND ONE THAT BIG?

SIMPLE. BURN A HOLE IN THE OZONE LAYER!

MORE, MORE! POINT STRAIGHT UP. LET THOSE CFC's FLOW!

LET'S BURN A LOVELY HOLE IN THE OZONE OVER ABERDEEN! LET IN SOME NICE ULTRAVIOLET RADIATION TO STERILISE THE HARBOUR!

BUT, SIR, WHAT ABOUT THE INCREASED RISK OF SKIN CANCER AS A RESULT?

LET ME SEE... THAT WOULD BE EPD'S CONCERN... OR IS IT HEALTH...

FEiGN

75

HOW DO WE KNOW WHETHER STERILISING ABERDEEN HARBOUR HAS MADE THE SEAFOOD SAFE?

WE CONDUCT A SCIENTIFIC TEST. WE GET A CONTROL GROUP TO EAT IMPORTED SEAFOOD, AND A TEST GROUP TO EAT LOCAL FISH, THEN SEE WHO GETS SICK.

WHO'S FOOLISH ENOUGH TO JOIN THE TEST GROUP? EVERYONE IN HONG KONG KNOWS THE SEAFOOD IS INFECTED, EXCEPT—

TOURISTS!!

JUMBO

THE GOVERNMENT TODAY DECLARED AN END TO THE SEAFOOD CHOLERA EPIDEMIC.

PORK RINDS

ACCORDING TO A SPOKESMAN, A HOLE IN THE OZONE LAYER HAS LED TO INCREASED LEVELS OF HELPFUL ULTRAVIOLET RADIATION AROUND THE TERRITORY.

PORK RINDS

NOT ONLY ARE LOCAL FISH STERILISED OF BACTERIA...

BTV

BUT THEY'RE NICELY BROWNED AS WELL.

77

THERE SHE IS, MY NEW COMPUTER! LOVELY, ISN'T SHE?

MM.

WHAT ARE YOU DOING WITH THE OLD ONE?

I GAVE IT TO CRYSTAL. NOWADAYS THEY SHOULD LEARN COMPUTER LITERACY AS YOUNG AS POSSIBLE. RUDY'S IN THERE SHOWING HER.

LET'S SEE ANOTHER ONE. TYPE: "SMUT@PORN.SOOZIE.DONKEY"

Mmmm...

WHAT ARE YOU THINKING, DARLING?

WHETHER ON MY NEW COMPUTER I SHOULD RESET "CONFIG.SYS" TO "FILES=40" AND IF I PREFER THE PROGRAM ICONS PURPLE OR AZURE. BE RIGHT BACK.

WOMEN...!

78

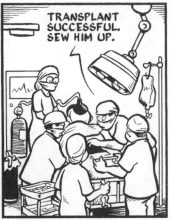

First reports came in of China's alleged use of executed prisoners' organs for transplants.
And Li Peng had a rumoured heart attack. Who could resist such an obvious gag setup?

WE'LL DISSOLVE THE POLITBURO! HOLD FREE NATIONAL ELECTIONS! BAN SPITTING! MAYBE I'LL RING CHRIS PATTEN FOR ADVICE.

COMRADE XIAOPING, DOCTORS ACCIDENTALLY TRANSPLANTED THE HEART OF A PRO-DEMOCRACY ACTIVIST INTO LI PENG. WHAT DO WE DO?

HE SAYS: "IT DOESN'T MATTER IF A CAT IS BLACK OR WHITE, AS LONG AS ... UH ... IT DOESN'T SCRATCH THE FURNI—"

mmblblbl KtsKlgf vjxm...

DID HE SAY BAN SPITTING? SHOOT HIM.

SEE? THE PARAMOUNT LEADER STILL HAS HIS LUCID MOMENTS.

WE NEED A NEW HEART TRANSPLANT FOR LI PENG IMMEDIATELY!

WHO'S UP FOR EXECUTION TODAY?

LET'S SEE... A PIMP, A DRUG SMUGGLER, A BICYCLE THIEF, AND A HONG KONG OWNER OF A SHENZHEN FACTORY.

HONG KONG REJOICES AS PLA MARCHES IN

People's Daily

TYPHOONS, FLOODS ARE BRITAIN'S FAULT

MM. FORGET THE HONG KONG FACTORY OWNER.

WHY?

STUPID! WE NEED SOMEONE WITH A HEART!

A RARE BLACK-FACED SPOONBILL SOARS MAJESTICALLY SOUTHWARD FROM THE FAR NORTH.

AN ANNUAL PILGRIMAGE OF OVER 2000 KILOMETRES, AS ITS ANCESTORS HAVE DONE FOR THOUSANDS OF YEARS, TO SPEND THE WINTER IN—

THUD

CRASH!!

A NEW GOLF COURSE & LUXURY LIFESTYLE DEVELOPMENT...?!

DAMN BIRDS! WHEN THEY GONNA PAVE OVER THAT STUPID MARSH ALREADY?

MAI PO MARSH

FEIGN

COME, EVERYONE. A DEVELOPER WISHES TO BUILD HIGH-RISES AND A GOLF COURSE NEXT TO MAI PO NATURE RESERVE. WE HAVE TO DO A REPORT.

Dept. of PREVARICATION & OBFUS...

PAPERWORK ALL READY?

MM. SURVEY REPORT... LANDS RECORDS... BUILDING PLANS...

WAIT, WHERE'S THE ENVIRONMENTAL IMPACT REPORT?

CURRENTLY MAKING AN IMPACT ON THE ENVIRONMENT.

Dept. of ...CATION and ...TION

Dept. of RIDICU... & ILL-CON... PROJEC...

RECYCLE BIN PAPER ONLY

FEIGN

WELL, I'M CERTAINLY GLAD IT'S NOT JARDINE'S WHO'S BUILDING A DEVELOPMENT IN MAI PO.

WHY? AFRAID CHINA WOULD OBJECT?

NO, I'M AFRAID THEY'D START TALKING ABOUT RELOCATING ALL THE BIRDS TO AN UNDERGROUND CAR PARK!

MR. SNEEDSLEY, IF WE GIVE THIS ONE DEVELOPER PERMISSION TO BUILD RIGHT AROUND MAI PO, IT WILL SET A PRECEDENT.

THE ENTIRE PLACE WILL BE SWARMING WITH PROPERTY DEVELOPERS!

PRECISELY, MISS WONG. MAI PO IS A BIRD SANCTUARY, AFTER ALL.

AND HONG KONG PROPERTY DEVELOPERS ARE NOTHING BUT VULTURES.

HEADS UP! THE CONSUMER COUNCIL IS COMING TO INSPECT OUR SUPERMARKET!

SUPER MARKET

QUICK! DUMP EVERYTHING THAT'S PAST ITS "USE BY" DATE!!

HAH?! WHAT ARE YOU DOING??!

WHAT YOU SAID. DUMPING EXPIRED ITEMS.

SEE? "1993 VINTAGE".

VSOP
ROSÉ
CHENIN BLANC
VIN French wi...

THE CONSUMER COUNCIL IS LOOKING INTO ALLEGATIONS OF PRICE FIXING BY THE MAJOR SUPERMARKETS.

SPECIAL Pears $26
Wine Sale
BEANS $5.90

HEH-HEH. YOU WON'T FIND THAT IN OUR COMPANY.

YEAH, THE WAY WE RAISE PRICES EVERY OTHER DAY, THE LAST THING YOU'D EVER ACCUSE US OF IS PRICE FIXING!

THE CONSUMER COUNCIL INVESTIGATES!

TSK, TSK, TSK. WHAT HAVE WE HERE?

SUPER MARKET

THESE JARS OF PEANUT BUTTER ARE EXACTLY ONE YEAR PAST THEIR "CONSUME BY" DATE.

WHAT DO YOU HAVE TO SAY ABOUT THAT?

♪ HAPPY BIRTHDAY TO YOU ♫ HAPPY BIRTHDAY TO YOU...

FEIGN

WE'VE HAD COMPLAINTS FROM CONSUMERS ABOUT WHOLE WHEAT BAKING FLOUR.

SUPER MARKET

THEY SAY YOU STOCKED IT FOR YEARS, THAT IT ALWAYS SOLD QUICKLY, AND YET YOU RECENTLY STOPPED CARRYING THE PRODUCT. WHY?

SUPER MARKET

GWAILO STUFF. ICK!

FAIR POINT.

FEIGN

87

LOOK HOW MANY LAYERS OF PRICE LABELS!

SALE CORN $29

MM. WE'RE DOING AWAY WITH THOSE. WE'RE GOING HI-TECH WITH OUR NEW BAR CODE READERS.

NO MORE MESSY STICKERS. JUST START THE COMPUTER'S CLOCK...

Employees Only

RICE Bun

AND IT AUTOMATICALLY RAISES PRICES EVERY 30 MINUTES!

BEEP! THE TIME IS 11:30... PRICES UP 3%...

Today's Prices

FEIGN

THIS SUPERMARKET REPEATEDLY RAISES PRICES ON OLD STOCK, YOU SELL EXPIRED ITEMS...

SUPER MARKET

YOU STOCK MERCHANDISE THAT SUPPLIERS PAY YOU TO SELL, RATHER THAN WHAT'S NECESSARILY THE BEST QUALITY OR VALUE.

YOU CERTAINLY DON'T GIVE VERY MUCH TO YOUR CUSTOMERS.

SURE WE DO!

TWENTY FREE PLASTIC BAGS WITH EVERY $10 PURCHASE!

FEIGN

88

CHINA IS AT IT AGAIN! THEY'RE EVICTING McDONALD'S IN BEIJING, ONLY TWO YEARS AFTER SIGNING A 20-YEAR LEASE.

OWmmno POTHOLES IN KOWLOON

RIVER VERDAN LIFE STORY

WAH! THAT'S GOOD NEWS.

HUH?

IF CHINA'S VIOLATING A 20-YEAR CONTRACT AFTER ONLY TWO YEARS...

RAT PUM BEER

THAT MEANS WE GOT A WHOLE FIVE YEARS BEFORE THEY NULLIFY THE 50-YEAR BASIC LAW!

FEIGN

The Beijing city government moved to evict McDonald's to make way for a commercial property development. This called into question the security of any contracts signed with the Chinese government.

COMRADE! McDONALD'S STILL REFUSES TO VACATE!

WHAT?! CALL IN THE 27TH ARMY!

TANKS ARE PRIMED AND IN POSITION, PREMIER LI!

THEN DO IT!!

COMRADES, GIVE THE ORDER!

...3 MEDIUM FRIES, 6 LARGE COKES, A McNUGGETS WITH MEXICAN SAUCE...

McDonald's

McDRIVE THRU

FEIGN

89

I READ IN THE PAPER— A RECENT STUDY SHOWS THAT CHINESE ARE THE MOST INTELLIGENT RACE ON EARTH.

WE HAVE HIGHER I.Q.'s THAN ANYONE ELSE.

WAH.

THEN GWAILO SHOP ASSISTANTS MUST BE REALLY REALLY **REALLY** STUPID!

TELL ME SOMETHING...

Dept. of PREVARICATION and OBFUSCATION

IF CHINESE ARE SUPPOSEDLY THE MOST INTELLIGENT RACE ON EARTH...

WHY IS IT THAT EVERY PERSON IN ALL OF HONG KONG AND CHINA...

STILL THINKS A LIFT COMES FASTER BY PRESSING BOTH THE UP AND DOWN BUTTONS?

repeated pushing

FEIGN

STUART, WHY DO MEN CHEAT ON THEIR WIVES?

I DON'T KNOW. MAYBE MONOGAMY ISN'T A NATURAL STATE FOR HUMANS. NO OTHER MAMMAL MATES FOR LIFE WITH A SINGLE PARTNER.

THE ONLY CREATURES WHO ARE FAITHFUL FOR LIFE ARE SWANS, SOME GEESE AND CERTAIN SPECIES OF DUCKS.

SOB. THIS WAS SOMEBODY'S DEVOTED WIFE OR HUSBAND.

SEE WHERE MONOGAMY GETS YOU?

SIGH... IT'S OVER FOR ME. MY WIFE IS THREATENING DIVORCE. MY MAINLAND MISTRESS IS DUMPING ME.

AND NOW THERE'S TALK OF A NEW LAW TO PUNISH MEN WHO KEEP MAINLAND CONCUBINES.

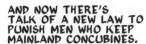

OH, THAT'LL NEVER PASS. HASN'T CHINA ALWAYS SAID IT WON'T TOLERATE ANY...

INTERFERENCE IN MAINLAND AFFAIRS.

95

STUART...

SHHH. JUST A MINUTE. I'M E-MAILING A FILE.

STUART!

YEAH, YEAH. FIVE MORE MINUTES.

WHERE YA GOIN'?

NEXT DOOR. TO BORROW THEIR COMPUTER.

TELNET to
stuart@fareast.com>

DINNER IS READY!!!

I'M DOING A FILE TRANSFER FROM GRAZ, AUSTRIA.

ISN'T IT INCREDIBLE WHAT YOU CAN DO WITH THE INTERNET?

IT'S AMAZING — ELECTRONS TRAVELLING ALL THE WAY FROM EUROPE, AROUND THE WORLD, AND POURING RIGHT INTO THIS ROOM!

WAI? IMMIGRATION? WE GOT A HOUSE FULL OF GWAILO ELECTRONS!

96

YOU'VE BEEN INTERNETTING FOR TWO HOURS!

ALL RIGHT, ALL RIGHT. TEN MORE MINUTES, 'TIL I FINISH WITH THIS NEWSNET GROUP.

TSK. COMPUTERS! I'M GOING OUT TO GET BREAST IMPLANTS.

HUH??

BECAUSE IT SEEMS NOWADAYS YOU PREFER SPENDING TIME WITH SOMETHING THAT'S FULL OF SILICON!

STUART, YOU NEVER CAME TO BED.

I WAS UP ALL NIGHT IN CYBERSPACE. I COULDN'T STOP.

I SAW SATTELITE PHOTOS OF MADAGASCAR, HEARD AL GORE'S VOICE, THREW SNOWBALLS AT SCIENTISTS, READ 'CALVIN AND HOBBES' IN DUTCH, LOOKED AT A GIRL'S BASKETBALL TEAM, JOINED THE CREW OF 'STAR TREK', LISTENED TO A ZAPPA OUTTAKE...

FUNNY. SAME THING HAPPENED TO ME LAST NIGHT.

YOU WERE ON THE INTERNET TOO?

NO, I WAS ON TEQUILA, LIGHTER FLUID, PROZAC AND KOOL-AID.

97

DISMEMBERMENT HAS ITS PRIVILEGES

AMERICAN EXCESS

Eat at Pat's

FEIGN

In a television ad, a major credit card company associated itself with a fancy shark fin restaurant. A public debate ensued about the cruel manner in which shark fins are harvested. The company later withdrew the ad, though not before these cartoons appeared.

FLOOP!

HE'S GOT DINER'S...VISA... NOPE, DON'T SEE THE OTHER ONE.

LET HIM GO.

LEAVE HOME WITHOUT IT!

SHARKS' REVENGE.

FEIGN

SHRIEK! ANOTHER MUTILATED SISTER!

THE BASTARDS TOOK HER FIN!

SHE'S STILL ALIVE. QUICK!

DANGER RAW SEWAGE

ABOUT YOUR REPLACEMENT-WITHIN-24-HOURS GUARANTEE...

AMERICAN EXCESS Card Centre

RATES

AN' IF I GO SWIMMING, THE SHARKS DON'T TOUCH ME 'CAUSE I EATEN SO MANY THEIR FINS.

NO SUCH CHANCE, BOZO!

AMERICAN EXCESS-- PROUD TO BE IDENTIFIED WITH THE MUTILATION AND AGONIZING DEATHS OF EARTH'S DWINDLING WILDLIFE.

MAN! FIRST THERE WERE THOSE SEXIST COGNAC ADS, THEN THAT OBNOXIOUS "I HATE YOU" PERFUME ADVERT. AND NOW THIS.

PITY OUR FINS AREN'T AS TASTELESS AS THE HONG KONG ADVERTISING BUSINESS.

DANGER RAW SEWAGE

PSST. HEY, BUDDY!

WE'RE LOOKING FOR THE OFFICES OF THAT COMPANY THAT'S PROUD TO ASSOCIATE ITSELF WITH MASS MURDER AND TORTURE.

SURE. GO HERE.

ATV

IF ADOLF WERE ALIVE HE'D ADVERTISE ON ATV

FEIGN

Local television station ATV used pictures of Hitler in a self-promotional ad campaign.

THERE THEY ARE. THE ONES WHO GLORIFY THE BUTCHERY OF OUR KIND.

WHAT DO WE DO NOW?

AMERICAN EXCESS

WE HAVE A CONFERENCE IN THE EXECUTIVE TOILET.

LISTEN UP, CLOWNIE! OUR FINS ARE WORTH HOW MUCH, RETAIL, IN THAT OVERBLOWN CHOWDER JOINT IN THE AD? AND IF WE CHARGED THAT AMOUNT ON AN AMEX CARD...

BAHAMAS HO! I HEAR THE NURSE SHARKS THERE ARE HOT!

AND WE STILL GOT 6000 FREQUENT FLYER MILES LEFTOVER!

IN-FLIGHT MENU

FEIGN

EXCUSE ME. I'M HERE ABOUT THE JOB OPENING.

SORRY, SUGAR. WE DON'T NEED NO NEW CHECKOUT GIRLS.

I'M TALKING ABOUT THE **ASSISTANT MANAGER** POSITION.

HAR HAR HAR! THAT'S ALWAYS BEEN A **MAN'S** JOB IN THIS SHOP, SWEETIE PIE!

NOW THEY TELL ME ABOUT THIS #@%!!✱✱# ANTI-SEX DISCRIMINATION BILL!

THE EMPLOYERS' EQUAL OPPORTUNITY GUIDELINES "FORBID DISCRIMINATION ON THE GROUNDS OF GENDER, AGE, MARITAL STATUS, RACE, DISABILITY OR NATIONALITY."

DOES THAT MEAN IF THERE WAS A TRANSSEXUAL, 95-YEAR-OLD, POLYGAMOUS, PYGMY, SPASTIC, BOSNIAN-SERB CITIZEN, YOU'D HAVE TO HIRE, ER... IT?

HA HA HA! DON'T HAVE TO WORRY TOO MUCH ABOUT THAT IN HONG KONG!

YOU OBVIOUSLY NEVER SEEN WHAT SLITHERS OFF THE LAMMA ISLAND FERRY.

TSK. LOOK AT THAT. THE BOSS IS CONSIDERING HIRING A *WOMAN* AS ASSISTANT MANAGER!

HE HAS TO, UNDER THE EQUAL OPPORTUNITY GUIDELINES.

HMF.

HEY, TOOTS. WANT TO REALLY IMPRESS THE BOSS? TELL HIM YOU GIVE MONEY TO THE DEMOCRATIC PARTY.

CHUCKLE. LUCKY THEY DELETED THE PART ABOUT "NO POLITICAL DISCRIMINATION".

FEIGN

RUDY IS ALL DEPRESSED ABOUT THIS EQUAL OPPORTUNITY ORDINANCE.

WHY? WHAT'S THE BIG DEAL? IT ONLY MEANS THAT MEN AND WOMEN HAVE TO BE TREATED THE SAME.

HE'S AFRAID THAT IF HE DECIDES TO GET MARRIED...

HE'LL BE REQUIRED TO GIVE EQUAL CONSIDERATION TO A MAN!

FEIGN

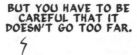

103

WAI?

MR. WONG RUDY MO-YUNG?

YOU HAVE BEEN SELECTED TO WIN A **DELUXE SUPER HOLIDAY!**

WAH!

ALL YOU HAVE TO DO IS SIT THROUGH A LENGTHY, IRRITATING, EXCRUCIATINGLY MIND-NUMBING HARD SALES PITCH!

OH, YOU MEAN THAT BROOKE SHIELDS PANTYHOSE COMMERCIAL!

FEIGN

WAH! JUST WON A DELUXE HOLIDAY! I GOT TO GO TO THEIR OFFICE TO PICK UP THE PRIZE.

TSK. SOUNDS LIKE ONE OF THOSE TIME-SHARE RESORT COME-ONS. HE'LL BE SUBJECTED TO A 3-HOUR HARD SALES PITCH.

TSK. YOU'RE SO PARANOID.

GOT ONE! FINALLY!

BEAM US UP, VRBLFX5:TN@!

FEIGN

104

106

WE CAN FINALLY REVEAL THE TRUE REASON THAT YOU WERE BROUGHT HERE

A RECENT SOLAR FLARE RENDERED ALL MALES ON OUR PLANET IMPOTENT. WE NEED YOU TO MATE WITH OUR FEMALES SO THAT WE MAY CONTINUE OUR RACE

SOUNDS COOL, BUT WHY ME?

WE WERE ORDERED TO CAPTURE THE EARTH MALE WITH MAXIMUM 'HUNK' APPEAL

LOOK! EEEK! IT'S BRAD PITT!

SCREE!

LUCKILY, ALL YOU EARTHLINGS LOOK ALIKE

RUD=EE, YOU ARE OUR FINAL HOPE. ALL OUR MALES ARE STERILE. YOU ALONE CAN REPOPULATE OUR PLANET.

LET ME GET THIS STRAIGHT— YOU WANT ME TO...ER...'DO IT' WITH THOUSANDS AND THOUSANDS OF WOMEN ALL AROUND YOUR WORLD?

AFFIRMATIVE

SORRY, YOU GOT THE WRONG GUY FOR THAT.

I AIN'T EVEN A CATHAY PACIFIC PILOT!

108

WHILE YOU WERE ASLEEP, WE REMOVED A HAIR, AND CLONED 10,000 DUPLICATES OF YOU TO MATE WITH OUR FEMALES

WAH! TEACH ME TO DO THAT!

YOU WISH TO POPULATE THE EARTH WITH CLONES OF YOURSELF?

NO, SO I CAN GO TO FLORIDA AND SELL COPIES OF RICHARD GERE TO ALL THE RETIRED WIDOWS!

HEY, GUYS, I GOT TO GET BACK TO EARTH.

BUT, RUD=EE, YOU JUST GOT HERE!

DON'T YOU WANT TO EXPLORE NEW GALAXIES, LEARN ADVANCED TECHNOLOGIES, SEE THE CENTRE OF THE UNIVERSE?

DISCOVER THE VERY SECRET OF TIME, MATTER, AND CREATION ITSELF?

HOW CAN YOU POSSIBLY LEAVE NOW??

TSK. THEY DON'T KNOW WHAT IT'S LIKE TO BE OUT OF CIGARETTES.

THIS PLANET SUCKS. *"RUD=EE PHONE HOME."*

HEY, WIENERBREATH! I BUILT A PHONE JUST FOR YOU!

THANKS, KID! DIAL 'ER UP...

HANG UP...

TSK. WHAT'S TAKING SO LONG?

YOU'RE 18,000 LIGHT YEARS FROM HOME. IT TAKES 36,000 YEARS FOR A RESPONSE.

HMF. REMIND ME WHEN I GET BACK TO EARTH— CANCEL THAT STUPID CALLBACK PHONE SERVICE!

DUE TO SPACE=TIME WARP, YOU WILL RETURN TO EARTH AT PRECISELY THE SAME TIME COORDINATES AS WHEN YOU LEFT

WAH! CAN WE GO BACKWARDS IN TIME TOO?

THEORETICALLY IMPOSSIBLE

WE WOULD BE CAUGHT IN A TIME LOOP: AN ENDLESS SERIES OF REPETITIONS OF REPETITIONS OF REPETITIONS...

FUNNY. TVB AND ATV GET AWAY WITH THAT.

111

112

GUNS AND CAR BOMBS IN AMERICA, POISON GAS IN JAPAN, TERRORISM AND FOOTBALL RIOTS IN EUROPE...

IT SEEMS LIKE HONG KONG IS THE ONLY PLACE LEFT WHERE YOU'RE SAFE FROM RANDOM VIOLENCE AND—

BONK!!!

YOU WERE SAYING...?

WHAT ARE YOU READING, MISS WONG?

ABOUT THOSE RIGHT-WING MILITIA GROUPS IN AMERICA.

CRAZY! A BUNCH OF WHITE MEN THINK THEY'RE LOSING JOBS AND PRIVILEGES TO OTHER ETHNIC GROUPS, SO THEY'RE STOCKPILING WEAPONS AND EXPLOSIVES. FRIGHTENING!!

THANK GOODNESS WE LIVE HERE, NOT AMERICA.

YES, I'M SURE YOU'RE RIGHT, MISS WONG.

Director

THEY'RE ON TO US!

IT'S STILL A BRITISH COLONY!

BAN LOCALISATION

GIVE ME the CANBERRA or Give me DEATH

113

THE FIRST GENERAL MEETING OF THE GWAILO ACTION COMMANDO KORPS (G.A.C.K.) IS HEREBY CALLED TO ORDER.

EXPAT POWER

LOCALISATIO IS MEDIOCRISAT

GENTLEMEN, OUR MISSION IS THREE-FOLD: FIRST, TO DEFEND THE PRIVILEGES INHERENT TO WHITE MEN, AS GOD INTENDED.

SECOND, TO END THE EVIL OF LOCALISATION IN BOTH PUBLIC AND PRIVATE SECTORS.

AND FINALLY, TO LICENCE AND MANUFACTURE OFFICIAL AUTHORISED G.A.C.K.® PLASTIC ACTION FIGURES!

HEAR HEAR!

THE EAST IS WHITE

FEIGN

SIGH... THERE WAS NO TIME LIKE THE GOOD OLD DAYS...

Gwailo Action Commando Korps   X

Endangered Species
EXPAT MALE

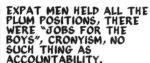

EXPAT MEN HELD ALL THE PLUM POSITIONS, THERE WERE "JOBS FOR THE BOYS", CRONYISM, NO SUCH THING AS ACCOUNTABILITY.

AND NO MATTER HOW INCOMPETENT ONE WAS, ONE WOULD NEVER FEAR FOR HIS JOB.

DECLARE PARKVIEW A WHITE HOMELAND

THERE'S STILL THE LEGAL DEPARTMENT, SIR.

I KNOW—LET'S DECLARE THE ATTORNEY GENERAL A GOD AND CALL OURSELVES A RELIGIOUS CULT!

FEIGN

114

SIR, WE JUST TRIED FOMENTING HATRED AND VIOLENCE ON THE RADIO LIKE THEY DO IN AMERICA, BUT THEY CUT US OFF WITH A PHIL COLLINS SONG.

GWAILO ACTION COMMAND KORPS

X-PAT

GOD is an EXPAT

FOOLS! YOU'RE USING THE WRONG TACTICS!

IF YOU WANT RADIO LISTENERS TO FEEL HATRED AND DISGUST...

YOU HAVE TO REQUEST MICHAEL BOLTON INSTEAD!

END BILINGUAL TV ENGLISH ONLY

FEIGN

Sneedsley's WHITE MALE'S HISTORY OF HONG KONG

FEIGN

1840-1841
Colony founded by White Men for the benefit of White Men. Prospers for next 100 years.

1941
Non-whites take over. Four years of misery and death.

1945
White Men back in charge. Peace and prosperity return.

1984
A 'Woman' bequeaths the Colony to evil Oriental despots.

JOINT DECLAR-ATION

1994
Non-White Non-Male becomes Chief Secretary. Property and stock markets go into free-fall.

STOP THE MADNESS! JOIN THE GWAILO ACTION COMMANDO KORPS!

BOYS, YOU'RE GOING TO BEIJING #2 PRISON.

WHAT??

PINCHBECK Public Relations

THEY'RE OUR CLIENTS, REMEMBER? THANKS TO U.S. PRESSURE, THEY NO LONGER EXPORT GOODS MADE BY FORCED PRISON LABOUR.

NOW THEY NEED SOME MARKETING ADVICE FOR A NEW PRODUCT LINE.

AND SO IF WE EXECUTE THE INMATES AND SELL THEIR ORGANS, NO PRISONER LABOUR INVOLVE!

YANKS BE HAPPY!

China's alleged sales of body parts from executed prisoners made world news. Reportedly, death row prisoners were kept in reserve, their executions timed to meet orders for specific transplant organs.

Y-YOU'RE SELLING THE PRISONERS' BODY PARTS?? THEY MUST BE READY TO RIOT!

NO, THEY HAPPIER THAN EVER.

BEIJING No. 2 PRISON

HOW CAN THAT B—

I TOLD YOU! WE NEVER BEAT INMATES IN THIS PRISON!!!

MIGHT DAMAGE HIS KIDNEYS—WORTH 30 GRAND APIECE!

THE KEY TO SUCCESS IN RETAIL IS **PRESENTATION**.

MISTER **K**IDNEY

INSTANT **BODY PARTS**

EXECUTING PRISONERS FOR THEIR ORGANS IS PRETTY GRUESOME. BUT IF YOU PRESENT IT RIGHT, MAKE THE CONSUMER MORE AT EASE...

WHAT YOU GOT IN MIND?

WELL, THERE'S THE HONG KONG SEAFOOD RESTAURANT APPROACH...

I'LL TAKE THE ONE ON THE LEFT.

HEART TRANS PLANT

SURGERY

HOW DO YOU PLAN TO FILL ALL THE EXPECTED ORDERS FOR TRANSPLANT ORGANS?

BODY PARTS

Property of BEIJING No. 2 Prison

NO WORRIES. WE GOT ENOUGH DEATH ROW PRISONERS ON RESERVE TO LAST US ANOTHER TWO YEARS.

WHAT HAPPENS AFTER THOSE RUN OUT?

BY THEN IT'LL BE 1997 AND WE GOT ALL THE DEMOCRATS, AND OVER A DOZEN CARTOONISTS!

FEIGN

117

EXCUSE ME, COMRADES. WHAT BLOOD TYPE ARE YOU?

"A-"

"O+"

"O-"

"AB+"

"AB+"? HM! AND WOULDN'T YOU SAY THAT LI PENG IS A FASCIST MURDEROUS DOG?

YEAH. HEH-HEH. BUT DON'T TELL ANY—

GOT THOSE CORNEAS FOR THE CLIENT IN KOWLOON TONG!

The above cartoon appeared on May 19, 1995. That evening, "The World of Lily Wong" was permanently cancelled.
Below is the final "Lily Wong" cartoon strip, May 20, 1995.

MRS. FARNSWORTH, I'M TAKING MYSELF OFF THE PRISONER ORGANS ACCOUNT.

ALOHA

PORK RINDS

Mister SWEETS

I CAN'T GO ON WITH IT. IT'S TOO MUCH GRUESOME DEATH, DOOM, SUFFERING...

AS YOU WISH. I'LL MOVE YOU TO THE "SUCK-UPS" CIGARETTES ACCOUNT.

YOU'RE STAYING WITH THE PRISONER ORGANS ACCOUNT?

AT LEAST IT'S KILLING YOU CAN JUSTIFY.

Mr. LENS

MR. KIDNEY

"KILL THE CARTOONS"

On May 19, 1995, I was on the phone half the day to Henry Wong in the Art Department of the *South China Morning Post*. We were ironing out last-minute technical problems in a new experimental system that Chief Artist Paul Best, Henry and I had developed to electronically transfer "Lily Wong" cartoons from my home studio directly into the newspaper's computerized page layout system. It was an idea we had discussed for months and had worked on gradually over the preceding six weeks. Thus I would complete the cartoons for the week (by pen and ink), scan them into my computer and upload them over the telephone lines to the *Post*, where Henry and Paul would reformat them and insert them on screen into their assigned page position. This system would enable us to have fine control over the image quality. And in any case, it was the direction that most publications were heading, with artwork and photos increasingly inserted electronically: the paperless newspaper!

After four hours of varied attempts that day, the transfer was complete. Shortly thereafter the re-formatting was done. It was a success! We had our system. The following Monday the first cyber-cartoon would appear in the paper.

At 8:00 that evening, Editor-in-chief David Armstrong approached Paul in the Art Department. Paul was excitied to show off what we'd done, as the editor had shown an interest in our progress over the past weeks. Paul announced to Armstrong that all the hard work had paid off: the new system worked perfectly!

"That's too bad," Armstrong replied. "Kill the cartoons."

Pages 121-123 contain the six "killed" cartoons that never appeared. That same evening I was in the midst of preparing a further six cartoons. I had finished the lettering and pencil sketches and was about to do the final inking. These are shown on pages 124-126, preserved in their unfinished state, they way they looked at the moment of Lily Wong's untimely demise.

121

I CAN'T BELIEVE THAT OUR GRANDMOTHER IS A CHINESE COMMUNIST OFFICIAL!

I THINK THAT'S COOL.

WHAT'S SO "COOL" ABOUT IT?

FOR ONE THING, SHE MUST DRIVE A *SUPER* RIGHT-HAND-DRIVE BMW!

FEIGN

Right-hand drive cars (for driving on the left side of the road) are not available in China. Yet scores of right-hand drive luxury cars, all stolen from Hong Kong, are seen in Chinese cities, many driven by party, army and police officials.

WERE YOU IN CONTACT WITH YOUR MOTHER AFTER YOU LEFT CHINA?

WE SENT HER MONEY ONCE. AND ANNOUNCEMENTS OF MY WEDDING, AND YOUR AND YOUR BROTHER'S BIRTHS... BUT NEVER GOT A REPLY.

I NEVER SAW OR HEARD FROM HER AGAIN. I DON'T EVEN KNOW IF SHE'S ALIVE OR DEAD.

OH, IT'S JUST THEM. I THOUGHT IT WAS TAXI DRIVERS ON TV WITH THEIR LATEST FARE RISE DEMAND.

WAAA BOO HOO

FEIGN

123

WOW! THERE ARE A **MILLION** OLD LADIES AROUND HERE! HOW DO WE START LOOKING FOR YOUR GRANDMOTHER?

BEGIN BY FINDING ONES WHO ARE, OR WERE, COMMUNIST OFFICIALS.

AND HOW DO YOU PROPOSE TO DO THAT?

SAY THAT YOU'RE CHRIS PATTEN AND SEE WHICH ONES ARE "TOO BUSY" TO MEET YOU!

DOES ANYONE IN THIS VILLAGE KNOW CHAN YI LING?

CHAN YI LING??

WAH! SHE MUST HAVE DONE SOMETHING REALLY TERRIBLE AGAINST THE VILLAGE.

NOT THAT WE KNOW OF.

BUT WE HEARD HER GRAND-DAUGHTER MARRIED A GWAILO!

THERE SHE IS!

PO-PO! I'M YOUR GRAND-DAUGHTER WONG LEI L—

FIRST YOUR GRANDFATHER ABANDONS ME!

WHACK!

THEN I WAS TORTURED AND HUMILIATED DURING THE CULTURAL REVOLUTION BECAUSE I HAD FAMILY IN HONG KONG!

WHAM WHAM

AND NOW THIS!! I CURSE YOU AND YOUR FAMILY FOR 10,000 YEARS!!

PTOO!

I TOLD YOU THE WIDE-SCREEN STEREO NICAM MULTI-SYSTEM FLAT-SCREEN TV WE BROUGHT ALSO NEEDED SUPER-WOOFER!

SCREEN EVISION

IN THE CULTURAL REVOLUTION THEY BEAT ME, DRAGGED ME THROUGH THE STREETS, SMEARED ME WITH EXCREMENT, MY HOUSE BURNED...

I WAS SENT TO A COAL MINE FOR TEN YEARS, STARVED, MOLESTED, STRIPPED OF MY IDENTITY, FORGOTTEN.

YOU'VE NEVER KNOWN SUCH SUFFERING IN HONG KONG AS WE HAVE IN CHINA.

SURE WE HAVE.

WHEN THERE'S A 10% DOWNTURN IN THE PROPERTY MARKET, YOU SHOULD HEAR THE TALK OF SUFFERING!

ARE YOU STILL A LEADING PARTY OFFICIAL IN THE DISTRICT?

NO, I STEPPED DOWN A FEW YEARS AGO.

AFTER A LIFETIME DEDICATED TO THE REVOLUTION, YOU MADE WAY TO LET YOUNGER BLOOD CARRY ON THE PROLETARIAN STRUGGLE. HOW NOBLE!

ACTUALLY, IT'S BECAUSE MY HANDS ARE FULL MANAGING THE THREE OFFICE BUILDINGS I OWN IN VANCOUVER.

BYE, GRANDMOTHER. I'M SO HAPPY TO KNOW MY PO-PO.

I'M HAPPY TOO, SUEN LUI.

YEAH, YOU DON'T SEEM LIKE A CADRE. I THOUGHT MOST COMMUNISTS WERE KILLER THUGS, LIKE THAT BUTTHEAD LI PENG.

YEAH, YEAH, I KNOW, I KNOW. "IF YOU CAN'T SAY ANYTHING NICE..."

GLOSSARY

1997	July 1, 1997: the date China ingests Hong Kong
Aberdeen Harbour	the one body of water even more polluted than Victoria Harbour
airport	new airport now being built; the most expensive unnecessary white elephant that ever existed in history
amah	house maid
ATV	Hong Kong television station
Basic Law	post-1997 constitution
Canberra	cruise ship ridden each year to England cost-free by retiring expatriate civil servants; this perk recently abolished
Canto-pop	Cantonese pop music
Cantonese	dialect spoken in Hong Kong and southern China
Cat Street	antique shop alley
Cathay Pacific	Hong Kong's main airline
CFC	chlorofluorocarbon; ozone-destroying agent in spray cans
Chan, Anson	Hong Kong's first female Chief Secretary
Chief Secretary	second-in-command in the Hong Kong government
CMB	China Motor Bus; known for daredevil drivers
Consumer Council	quasi-government consumer watchdog group
CRC	Cooperative Resources Centre; precursor to the "Liberal" Party
Daya Bay	site of Chinese nuclear power plant just upwind of Hong Kong
Democratic Party	pro-democracy party; largest political party in Hong Kong
dollar	One Hong Kong dollar = US$0.13
ECU	European Currency Unit
EPD	Environmental Protection Department
expat	expatriate; normally refers to Caucasian foreigners

EYT	"Enjoy Yourself Tonight"; TV variety show
Giordano's	clothing retail chain founded by anti-Beijing businessman Jimmy Lai
Guangdong	Chinese province adjacent to Hong Kong; also known as Canton
Guangzhou	Chinese major city; also known as Canton
Guilin	city in China
gwailo	what Cantonese call foreigners (literally: "demon man")
gwaipoh	female gwailo
Honkie	Singapore slang term for Hongkongers
I I	illegal immigrant
Index	Hang Seng Index; stock price indicator
Jardine's	one of Hong Kong's founding companies; disliked by China for being "pro-British"; also instigator of the Filipina relocation scheme (see "underground car park")
Joint Declaration	1984 pact in which China *declared* that Britain should hand over the *joint*
Liberal Party	party of far-from-liberal politicians
Joint Liaison Group	official Sino-British negotiating team on Hong Kong matters
Kowloon Tong	high-rent district in Kowloon peninsula
Lamma Island	low-rent island popular among young transient foreigners
Lan Kwai Fong	trendy nightclub district popular among foreigners
Lee, Martin	leading pro-democracy politician
Li Peng	Chinese Premier; architect of the 1989 Tiananmen Square massacre
Li, Ronald	former Director of the Hong Kong Stock Exchange
Lu Ping	Communist Chinese official in charge of Hong Kong affairs
Mai Po	wildlife preserve in the New Territories; currently under threat from proposed property development
Mark Six	twice-per-week lottery
MFN	Most Favoured Nation trading status with the United States
New Territories	area leased from China in 1898; now a gathering place for unbridled development, illegal immigrants and wrecked cars

Patten, Chris	Governor of Hong Kong 1992-
PLA	People's Liberation Army
po po	maternal grandmother
PRC	People's Republic of China
Preliminary Working Committee	sycophants and quislings appointed by Beijing to set up the post-1997 Hong Kong government
putonghua	Mandarin; official dialect in China
PWC	Preliminary Working Committee (see above)
quinella	horse race betting term
Shenzhen	Chinese city on the border with Hong Kong
shine shoes	Chinese equivalent of the English term "to bootlick"
Statue Square	favourite Sunday gathering place for Filipinos
suen lui	granddaughter (daughter's daughter)
TVB	Hong Kong television station
underground car park	where a certain major corporation suggested relocating Filipina maids on Sundays to clear them from view in Statue Square
United Democrats	precursor to the Democratic Party
Victoria Harbour	harbour so polluted that even the cholera germs gasp for breath
wai	hello (telephone greeting)
yuan	Chinese currency
Zhongnanhai	central government compound in Beijing

LARRY FEIGN began his cartooning career at the age of seven, when his "Hoiman the Mouse" appeared regularly in his primary school magazine. When the venture folded in Fifth Grade, his career went downhill for the next 16 years. Casting aside a promising future as a brain surgeon and/or lawyer at the age of ten, he then proceeded to further disappoint his mother by meandering through a series of other professions, including kindergarten teacher, ice cream maker, rock-and-roll violinist and petrol station toilet cleaner. Meanwhile, he dropped out of the University of California (Berkeley), finished his B.A. at Goddard College (Vermont), and again dropped out, from the University of Hawaii. Then, one warm tropical day in 1980, he was "discovered" in Honolulu, and hasn't put down a pen since. He has worked as a caricaturist at Waikiki Beach, animator in Hollywood, illustrator and newspaper cartoonist. He washed ashore in Hong Kong in 1985, and currently lives on Lantau Island with his wife Cathy (no, she is not Lily Wong) and children Ivan and Annika.

THE WORLD OF LILY WONG can be seen daily (in re-run) outside of Hong Kong in Malaysia's *New Straits Times* and on the Internet's World Wide Web (http://www.asiaonline.net/lilywong.html). Lily has appeared in numerous publications world-wide, including *The New York Times*, *Los Angeles Times*, *Newsweek*, *Business Week*, *The Atlantic*, *The Economist*, *Der Spiegel* and *Komsomolskaya Pravda* (Russia). Larry, and Lily, won Hong Kong's "Best Cartoonist" award in 1988, the only year such an award has ever been given in the colony.

BY THE SAME AUTHOR

AIEEYAAA!
AIEEYAAA, Not Again!
The World of Lily Wong
Quotations from Lily Wong
The Adventures of Superlily
Postcards from Lily Wong
How The Animals Do It
Hong Kong Fairy Tales

with Nury Vittachi:
Execute Yourself Tonite!